THE
SNOW
BALL

**

Also by A. R. Gurney, Jr.

NOVELS
The Gospel According to Joe
Entertaining Strangers

PLAYS
The Rape of Bunny Stuntz
The Comeback
The Golden Fleece
The David Show
The Problem
The Love Course
The Open Meeting
The Old One-Two
Scenes from American Life
Children
Who Killed Richard Cory?
The Wayside Motor Inn
The Middle Ages
The Dining Room
The Golden Age
What I Did Last Summer

THE
SNOW
BALL

A. R. Gurney, Jr.

A BELVEDERE BOOK

ARBOR HOUSE
New York

C. 2

Library of Congress Cataloging in Publication Data

Gurney, A. R. (Albert Ramsdell), 1930–
The Snow Ball.

I. Title.
PS3557.U82S6   1984   813'.54   84-10971
ISBN 0-97795-621-9

Manufactured in the United States of America

10 9 8 7 6 5 4 3 2 1

This is a work of fiction. Any similarity to persons living or dead is
purely coincidental and exists solely in the reader's mind.

To my mother

THE
SNOW
BALL

**

Middle-aged alumnus of a pre-World War
II dancing class resurrect the annual
end of the year ball and reunite the
star dancing partners of the group.

1

**

Jack Daley and Kitty Price were the best dancers in Buffalo. There was absolutely no doubt about that. It took your breath away to watch them. A kind of special space would emerge around them on the dance floor, as other couples moved away to give them room, and before long people would be shrugging apologetically, and separating from their partners, and simply standing around to watch. And when Jack and Kitty finished, usually with a quiet little dip or twirl, there was always applause.

They weren't so good when they were dancing with someone else. When another boy cut in on Kitty, she'd be light on her feet and follow fairly well, but she always seemed a little vague, a little distracted, and more often than not, she'd get into trouble on the turns. And the girls used to say

11

that when they danced with Jack, they always had the sense that he was looking over their shoulders, looking for Kitty, yearning for the time when he could dance with her again. "It's a shame," they'd say. "He could lead you to heaven, if only he wanted to. And if that was where you wanted to go."

But together Jack and Kitty were unbeatable. Nobody else came close to them. Nobody else even tried. For almost a decade there, in the center of the century, they ruled the roost. They won the top prize at the dancing school Cotillion, several special awards at the coming-out parties, and finally, the Gertrude Palmer Cup at the Snow Ball.

Years later, Jack and Kitty cropped up as the main topic of conversation after dinner at Cooper Jones's fiftieth birthday party, which his wife Liz gave for him in their house on Middlesex Road. A few of the old gang were there, the ones who hadn't moved away, and once they'd gotten through the toasts and the poems and the dessert and the Sanka, they moved into the living room where there was even some talk of rolling back the rug, putting on the old records, and trying to dance. They finally didn't, of course, but Cooper brought out some liqueurs, and Liz fixed up the fire—it was a cold January night—and people put their feet up and talked about Jack and Kitty instead, and the Snow Ball.

It was a most pleasant way to end the evening. None of them had thought much about the old days for quite a while, and as the conversation rolled around the room, each person adding a detail, a comment, a remembered incident, they found themselves feeling especially close to each other, like exiles from a remote and forgotten land. The fire helped, and the cognac, and the fact that Cooper had now travelled fifty years toward the grave, so that when they finally said their good-byes, they embraced each other with a special warmth and fervor.

Lucy Dunbar, who had been lonely and disheartened ever since her divorce, was the last to leave. "We may have stayed too long," she said, and she actually had tears in her eyes.

"Not at all," said Cooper politely. He would have automatically asked her to stay for another drink if Liz hadn't immediately added, "Well, it's late. I'll say that."

"Yes, and we have miles to go before we sleep," sighed Lucy. She hugged Liz, and then gave Cooper a long, damp kiss on the lips. Then she drew her overcoat around her—the old Persian lamb she had inherited from her mother—and left.

So the party ended. Cooper and Liz locked the door, put on the burglar alarm, and began to clean up. Their guests picked their way down the slippery sidewalks to their cold cars and the bleak, wintry streets of Buffalo.

You'd think that would be all there was to it: a brief, nostalgic interlude at the end of a small party for old friends in winter. But as it turned out, that was only the beginning. A few days later, Cooper received a telephone call at his office from Lucy.

"I'm sorry to bother you at work," she said, "but did you read today's paper?"

"I thought I did," Cooper said.

"Did you read page thirteen, under Local News?"

Cooper could hear the newspaper rattling in the background. "Tell me what it says."

"Read it and call me back," Lucy said. "It makes me even sadder than I was at your party."

So Cooper went and got the paper from Miss Kovac, his secretary, read page thirteen carefully, even though he had at least glanced at it before. A murder coming out of the domestic difficulties of an unemployed Bethlehem Steel worker in Lackawanna. A new bond issue to repair the decaying infrastructure—the sewers, the water lines, the streets—in the downtown Buffalo area. An article on the Japanese locust as a possible substitute for the American elm. And finally, down in the lower righthand corner, a small squib announcing that the Downtown Rehabilitation Committee was already making plans for a "Winterfest" to occur a year from now and to celebrate the refurbishment of the old George Washington Hotel.

Cooper couldn't quite figure out which of these items would make Lucy so sad. He called her back when he had a chance, but she said the issue was too complicated and important to discuss over the telephone, so they agreed to meet at the Saturn Club for lunch the following day.

The Saturn Club was always a good place to meet. You didn't have to wait, the service was good, and the food at least passable. It was equidistant from the downtown area and the Delaware Avenue district where many of its members lived. Most important, you could meet a woman there without people thinking you were having an affair. You were bound to see all sorts of people you knew at the Saturn Club, whereas if you met at the Anchor Bar or Jake's or the new Hyatt, you'd only see one or two, and that could lead to trouble.

Lucy was waiting for him in the main lounge when he arrived. She was already nursing a Perrier, which she took with her as they made their way through the dining room. They both nodded automatically to Burt Brisbane who was having lunch with his son Archie on vacation from Exeter, and those four young doctors who played paddle tennis every day at noon, and old Mrs. Sidway, who was having her food cut for her by her trained nurse. Lucy headed for a table in the corner where they wouldn't be interrupted, and after they'd ordered their salads and club sandwiches, she put down her menu, looked at Cooper, and sighed deeply.

"What's the matter, Lucy?" Cooper asked.

"Don't you know?"

"Tell me."

"This so-called Winterfest thing," said Lucy.

"Ah."

"Doesn't it make you just a little bit sad, Cooper?"

"Sad?"

"Has anyone called you about it? Has anyone called me? Has anyone we know"—she glanced furtively around the room—"been even remotely consulted?"

"I don't know," said Cooper.

"Well, *I* know," Lucy said. "I've checked. The answer is obvious. None of us—not one—has been asked to help organize these festivities. And that is *our* hotel!"

"It's not our hotel, Lucy."

"I consider it ours. We went to dancing school there. We held the Snow Ball there. My grandparents had their wedding reception there. My great-grandmother danced with President Grover Cleveland in that very ballroom. My father used to have lunch in the Erie dining room every day, Monday through Friday, for over fifty years! And you, too, Cooper! Your family is just as connected to the George

15

Washington as mine is. I'll bet somebody in your family *built* it, for God's sake!"

"They didn't build it, Lucy."

"Well they bought it or sold it or something. The point is, we're all very connected to that particular piece of real estate."

Their food came. Cooper eyed his club sandwich, wondering how he could take a bite of it without always feeling quite so much like a great white shark.

"Do you know when they're giving it?" said Lucy, picking at her salad. "This will break your heart."

"Giving what?" said Cooper, looking for his napkin.

"This Winterfest thing, or whatever it's called. Cooper, sweetheart, pay attention. You're getting vague in your old age. They are giving it the first Friday after Christmas."

"So?"

"So? So? Cooper, are you getting Alzheimer's disease? That was the exact date we used to have the Snow Ball. We even talked about it last week at your party."

"Oh. Right."

"That was *our* date. The ballroom was ours. And those people on that committee are going full steam ahead and ignoring us completely. I could cry."

Cooper's mouth was full of sandwich so he could do nothing but nod, but that obviously was the wrong response, so he shifted quickly to shaking his head in dismay. The lunch went on, and soon it became apparent what Lucy wanted him to do: get on that damn Downtown Rehabilitation Committee and take up her cause.

"I've done some scouting around," Lucy said. "The chair-

16

man happens to be your friend Saul Radner, who was appointed by our nice liberal mayor. Now I think the least you can do is call Mr. Radner and tell him that an important element in this city has been totally disregarded, and he'd better repair the damage immediately."

"Why me?" mumbled Cooper, like Moses before him. "Why don't you call him yourself?"

"Because I don't *know* him, Cooper. And you do. Now do you feel any sense of responsibility here? Or not?"

Cooper finished his coffee and put down his napkin. "Even if I got on that committee," he said, "what would we want?"

Lucy looked at him and got up. She seemed to think he was teasing.

"I'm going to be late for work," she said. "They practically make me punch a clock." Ever since her divorce, she worked part time in a little book store on Elmwood Avenue, in order to make ends meet.

Cooper followed her out of the dining room, and helped her on with her coat. "Seriously, Lucy," he said. "What do we really want to have happen?"

"I know what *I* want, Cooper. I'm not sure I can speak for *you*." She was buttoning up her coat. "I want to bring it back."

"Bring what back?"

"The Snow Ball, Cooper." She turned at the front door, and once again her eyes got a little misty, as they had the other night at his birthday party. "And I also want to bring back Jack and Kitty."

"Bring them *back?*"

"Well, why not? Everyone else in the world seems to be

17

dragging out a tradition or two. Let's get in on the *game*, Cooper. Or else, let's just throw in the towel, and sit on the sidelines, and let everyone call us white bread."

She looked at him long enough for that to sink in, and then she was out the door, holding her collar, staggering against the wind which came blasting down Delaware Avenue.

2

The George Washington Hotel.

The Snow Ball.

Dancing school.

These things all went together, and now, after Cooper's lunch with Lucy, they began to roll around in his head. It had been years since he had thought about them at all. The George Washington was a dark derelict of a building, lost behind the newer structures at the far end of downtown. The Snow Ball was a vague memory. And dancing school—how long had it been since he thought of that? And yet, my God, he must have attended the damn thing for three or four years. That was where he first knew Lucy, and where he met his wife Liz, and that was where Jack Daley first danced with Kitty Price.

19

How old were they all when they went to dancing school? Cooper could be very specific about his age when his family first started going over to Canada in the summer, or when he was sent to camp, or when he had scarlet fever. But dancing school? It seemed like a strange, floating island in the stream of his life, and it was hard to anchor it chronologically.

He asked his mother if she knew. He stopped by her apartment to see her at least once a week, and this time he had a very specific question.

"How old was I when I went to dancing school?"

"Dancing school?" said his mother. "What brought *that* up?"

"How old was I when I went?"

"Oh, heavens. I don't know. I suppose we started you off when you were about ten."

"Why then?"

"I have no idea, Cooper," said his mother. "I suppose that made you old enough to behave and young enough not to refuse." She was a little impatient because she wanted to eat her dinner early and watch the Sabres game on TV.

So he was about ten. That sounded right. He did remember that dancing school happened on Saturdays. It was the climax, or rather the anticlimax, to a long day. He and his friends would gather at the Saturn Club every Saturday morning at eleven to swim, raucous and naked in the echoey old pool, thick with chlorine and disinfectant. Then, after shivering red-eyed for a half an hour in the showers, they'd invade and occupy Smither's drugstore for peanut butter sandwiches and vanilla milk shakes. After that, it was on to the movies at the old Shea's Elmwood Theatre, where they'd settle into the red mohair seats, draping their legs over the backs of the seats in front of them, defying the ushers to make them sit up, whistling and cheering when the lights finally went down, booing Hitler in the newsreels, applauding Flash Gordon in the serial, throwing Cracker Jacks at the girls down in front during the boring parts of the second feature, making popping noises with their fingers in their cheeks when the main feature ended with a final kiss, then home by bus for a bath and a quick supper before they struggled into their white shirts and gartered socks and dark blue suits for—gasp, sigh, groan—*dancing school.*

"Do I have to go?"

"Of course you have to go. Everybody goes to dancing school."

"Duane Larkin doesn't go."

"That is Duane's problem. It's not yours. Now hold still while I tighten your tie."

Because this was during the war, and you had to be careful about gas, their mothers took turns driving them down to the George Washington, and picking them up afterwards, and even taking them to Smither's for an ice cream soda, if there was no fighting in the car. Sometimes they *would* fight, though, and whisper evil words like *bitch* and *bastard* because they were crowded and angry and frustrated after an evening at dancing school. Then their mothers would set their jaws and drive right past the drugstore, even though it caused groans and pummelings and general complaining until everyone got home.

Still, back they went the following week. War or peace, snow or sleet, in sickness and in health, you went to dancing school on Saturday nights from October through May. There was no way out, unless you had a serious temperature

21

or an obvious case of the mumps. You went, that's all. You went, just as you went to Charlie the Barber every six weeks, or to Miss Bacon the dental hygienist every six months, or to the shore of some large body of water every summer. You went, as your parents, and in many cases your grandparents, had gone before you. You went down to the old George Washington Hotel, where Mr. Van Dam, a gruff, rotund, elderly Dutchman in a natty suit of tails, rented the ballroom and for several centuries had been teaching Buffalo how to dance.

Cooper began to remember it all. They'd arrive, stamping the snow from their galoshes, avoiding the sneering looks of the bellboys in the already decaying lobby, to gather in the men's cloakroom by the stairs, milling, elbowing, jostling each other like steers in the stockyards, while across the hall, Mrs. Van Dam, their tormentor's wife, guarded the girls, brooding moodily in a gilt chair in front of the powder room, producing safety pins when needed, advice when not, stealing an occasional and disagreeable glance at her husband, who might be recovering from the beginner's class by having a quick snort from a silver flask underneath the stairs.

Forty years later, Cooper still shuddered as those days came rolling back into his memory. He saw himself once again packed into his dark suit, packed into that cloakroom, twenty or thirty preadolescent boys pulling at their collars, pushing at each other, playing keep-away with somebody's hat, wrestling among the urinals, slamming against the stalls, until there would be a great harrumphing cough from Mr. Van Dam in the corridor, and Mrs. Van Dam would start cackling and clapping her hands, and somehow they found themselves lining up and pairing off with the girls and marching sheepishly through the lobby of the hotel and up the marble staircase, until soon they could hear Mr. Cromeier thumping away at the piano—"Pomp and Circumstance" or the "Grand March" from *Aida*—and then in they'd come, now making a half-hearted attempt to keep time with the music, into the mirrored ballroom with the glittering sconces and slippery floor, where Mr. Van Dam and Mrs. Foster, who wore an evening dress and was the hostess and got a rake-off for her kids by being so, were waiting in the center of the floor to shake hands.

Then they'd separate, separate once again, boys to the right, girls to the left, coming to a halt on opposite sides of the room, standing, waiting, each in front of a small, stiff-backed gilt chair, until Mr. Cromeier, with uncanny timing, had somehow managed to end his endless march just as the last two or three girls who didn't have partners had found their seats as well. In the sudden silence that followed, they'd watch Mr. Van Dam bow to Mrs. Foster, offer her his arm, and conduct her to a seat in a small area behind a low balustrade, where she would sit patiently for the rest of the evening among those few other parents who were sadistic enough to come to watch.

Mr. Van Dam, meanwhile, would now be surveying his charges, moving up and down the opposed lines of stiff boys and tremulous girls, his black Malacca cane, or swagger stick, or whatever it was, held behind his back, twitching erratically and suspiciously like a cat's tail, as little beads of sweat already began to appear on the folds of the back of his neck over his starched white collar, reminding them of the cruel Sergeant in *Beau Geste* who had strutted in front of his doomed troops at the Elmwood Theatre that very same afternoon.

"The young ladies may be seated," he'd say, and Cooper now realized, forty years later, how carefully conceived that expression was. To "be seated" was not to "sit down." Sitting down implied volition, effort, labor. Dogs sat down when you told them to. Cleaning women sat down in kitchens at the end of a long day. But young ladies in dancing school were simply to be, intransitively and mysteriously, seated. And so, with a general rustling of silk and taffeta, and an occasional enticing flash of petticoat, the young ladies sat.

"The young gentlemen may now take their seats," Mr. Van Dam would then say, and lately Cooper found himself thinking about this, too. He noted the "now," for example, conveying the clear understanding that the boys couldn't sit until the girls had, as if the sitting process which had so delicately occurred across the dance floor were so refined and so complicated that it might require sudden masculine aid, and therefore men were supposed to stand at the ready until it had been completed. Cooper also noticed that the boys were to "take" their seats, seize them actively, possess them, the active verb hinting at the raw, rapacious natures which were at this point to be directed at chairs, rather than at the young lovelies who were settling their feathers opposite them.

And so the boys would take their seats, and sit, except for the time when Freddie Wilder had sneaked in ahead of time and placed thumbtacks on all the chairs, causing several boys suddenly to stand up. Mr. Van Dam, of course, guessed immediately who did it, and grabbed Freddie by the ear, and led him firmly to the door, and told him not to show up for three whole weeks, the lucky duck, and then turned to the rest of the boys and told them to take their seats again, immediately, which they immediately did.

Back it came, back it all came to Cooper Jones, in these strange days after his fiftieth birthday, as he drove to work, drove home, snoozed in his chair after dinner. "We will now review the basic two-step," Mr. Van Dam would say, and with surprising grace for such an old and portly man, he would glide across the polished floor in front of the seated rows of boys and girls, demonstrating "one-and-two-and-slide-and-two-and-small-steps-two-and," until he reached the raised podium where Mr. Cromeier was poised anxiously over the piano, hands at the ready, waiting for the nod to begin.

"The young gentlemen will rise."

They did.

"The young ladies will rise."

They did.

"Mr. Cromeier, if you please."

Mr. Cromeier played.

"And-one-and-two-and-slide-and-two," and they'd all start clumping around the garish, gilded room in a huge circle, like galley slaves in *The Sea Hawk* or convicts in *The Big House*, lashed together with invisible chains, concentrating, or at least trying to concentrate, on the beat and their feet. Cooper would occasionally glance in shame and horror at his own ghostly and distorted reflection in the mirrored walls as he stumbled past, but he tried never to glance at Mr. Van

Dam, who stood slowly rotating in the center of the room, grimly tapping his cane like Blind Pugh in *Treasure Island*, waiting to pounce, to single out some poor boy, to grab his arm in a steely grip and force him to turn and slide and step and slide until he damn well got it right.

Sometimes, as all this came back to him, Cooper wondered whether it was even true. It was so remote, so strange, so long ago. "Maybe I dreamed it," he thought. "Maybe it's an echo of some awful previous existence. How could I have been there and done those things? How could I actually have allowed myself to be pressed into such servitude, pushed and squeezed into such a cruel and dehumanizing ritual, presided over by a drunken old fascist, week after week, year after year? Didn't I protest? Didn't I rebel? My own sons would have taken one look at the proceedings and headed for the hills. Why didn't I? What did I think I was doing? Where was I going? What was the point?"

And then he thought of Jack Daley and Kitty Price, and how they met at dancing school, and won the prize at the end-of-the-year Cotillion, and more prizes on up through the Snow Ball. And somehow it all made perfect sense.

3

Saul Radner and Cooper Jones were good friends, or had become so over the past few years. They had grown up in different sections of Buffalo and didn't even meet each other until they were in their mid-twenties. In their youth, Cooper had heard the advertisements on the radio for Radner's Furniture, of course, and Saul had seen the real estate signs all over town put up by Dunlop, Potter, and Jones, but there was no real reason for them to have met in those distant days. Both Saul and Cooper were considered to be "scions" of distinguished old Buffalo families, and their parents certainly knew of each other and nodded at each other at the Buffalo Philharmonic or the theater, but that was about it. Saul went to Bennett High School while Cooper went to Nichols Country Day. On Saturdays, Saul went to Hebrew school and Shea's Colvin and various bar mitzvahs, while Cooper went to the Saturn Club and Shea's Elmwood and dancing school. Nichols played Bennett in several sports, so you'd think their paths might have crossed in manly competition, but Saul played basketball and Cooper played hockey, so they didn't meet then either. Later, Saul went to the University of Michigan, and Cooper, like his father, got into Brown.

They met, actually, in the Navy, or rather as they were being mustered out of the Navy in San Francisco, after the Korean War. Cooper had been a lieutenant (jg) on a destroyer escort stationed off Japan, and Saul had been a supply officer in the Philippines. There they were, stark naked, undergoing their final physicals, when a medical corpsman, looking at their records, pointed out they came from the same town. They looked at each other and struck up a tentative conversation as they went down the line, and their common yearning to go home caused an immediate affection between them, overriding the immediate indignity of being examined for syphilis and piles.

Cooper had already bought a car, and Saul agreed to share the gas, so as soon as they were in their civilian clothes, off they went, heading east. As they crossed the vast reaches of America, they compared notes about their lives back home in Buffalo, and found it endlessly fascinating that they could have grown up together in such a relatively small city and lived such relatively similar lives, and never have met till now.

"It's a great country," said Cooper.

"And a small world," said Saul as they drove along.

When Cooper married Liz, Saul, of course, was invited, and ditto when Saul married Judy. As their children were born, they gave presents and so forth, and they'd go to each other's houses for dinner at least every six months. Saul and Judy weren't invited to Cooper's fiftieth birthday party because that was really just the old, old gang, and when Cooper and Liz dropped in on Saul's house after his father died, they felt a touch out of place among his immediate family. But still, theirs was a good relationship and it had lasted quite a while.

Their daily lives continued to be somewhat different, of course. Cooper went into his father's real estate business, and Saul inherited his father's furniture store. Cooper kept things going, but Saul expanded his operations considerably. Dunlop, Potter, and Jones maintained their fine old offices in the Ellicott Square Building downtown while Radner's Furniture sold their store downtown and established themselves in several plazas and shopping malls in the suburbs. Cooper was appointed head of the House Committee at the Buffalo Tennis and Squash Club, while Saul chaired the Symphony Drive for several years and served on the boards of both the Art Gallery and the Science Museum. As far as politics were concerned, Cooper didn't have much to do with them. He left the Republican party during the Goldwater-Johnson campaign and stayed a registered Independent from then on in. Saul, on the other hand, was continuously and actively involved in the Democratic party at the local level, and attended several statewide conventions.

In the winter months, once a week, Saul and Cooper would get together to play squash. They'd play either at the Athletic Club, where Saul belonged, or the Tennis and Squash, where Cooper did. There were rules in both organizations about having the same guest so often, but everyone looked the other way in this case. There was such obvious reciprocity, and the two men enjoyed playing together so much. There was something about that particular sport—the stark white walls, the thin red lines, the smooth ball, the civilized and deferential rules—which appealed to them both. Cooper played with a kind of elegant defensive finesse, and Saul played with aggressive and dogged tenacity, and somehow they managed to occupy the same space at the same time and infuse each game with excitement and suspense. Sometimes, though neither would admit it for a minute, each felt he was playing on behalf of his "people"—that there, in that small white box, a huge ethnic contest was going on between thy nation and mine. The game could get extremely heated then, with lets called and counter-lets, and occasional strong arguments, but they always came out shaking hands and joking about it on the way to the showers.

They'd always have a beer afterwards, too, wrapping their towels around them and settling into cool leather chairs, chewing the fat, as Cooper put it, or schmoozing, according to Saul. Cooper had taken a humanities course at Brown, and Saul had minored in philosophy at Michigan, so they had a fine old time arguing about books, and movies, and ideas, and even Israel, though this could be a particularly tricky subject. They also loved to compare notes on their parents and their children, how they were brought up, how they hoped to pass things on. After a second beer, they'd arrive at profound conclusions about their similarities and differences.

"I believe in circles, you believe in straight lines," Cooper would say. "I believe the world is worse than it was. You believe it will be better. I'm a Greek yearning for a Golden

Age. You're a Jew in search of the Promised Land. What is Athens to Jerusalem?" He remembered some of these phrases from a course in college.

Saul might respond with some quote from Erich Fromm or Martin Buber, and they'd bat that around for a while until it was time to get up and get dressed. They'd drive home in separate cars to have dinner with their families, inwardly congratulating themselves on the breadth of their democratic vision and relishing their abiding friendship.

It was during one of these beers after one of these games that Cooper brought up the issue of the Downtown Rehabilitation Committee. Lucy Dunbar had telephoned him twice since they had had lunch, and Cooper felt that this was probably the best context in which to broach the subject. They were at Saul's club this time, and this time Cooper had lost the match, so perhaps that made him a little touchier than usual.

"Hey," Cooper said, "I hear you're chairing another committee."

"What committee?" Saul said.

"I read about it in the paper. Downtown redevelopment. George Washington Hotel. Some kind of winter festival."

"Oh, that."

"Who's on it?" Cooper asked.

"On it?"

"Who's on the committee, Saul?"

Saul obviously didn't want to talk about it much. "Oh, we rounded up the usual suspects."

"Who are they?"

"You wouldn't know them, Cooper."

"Name names. Give me a chance. Or is it top secret?"

"No, it's not top secret," said Saul, and he named his committee. There was Angela Montini, whose father ran a large construction company and whose brother was the judge. There was Tad Kowalski, a local union leader for the steelworkers who had twice been narrowly defeated for School Committee on an antibusing platform. There was Doctor Arthur Johnson, who was black. "And there's me, that's all," said Saul.

And of course Saul was right. Cooper didn't know any of them. Except Saul.

"Why didn't you ask me?" Cooper said, with a slight laugh.

"You?"

"Me. I wouldn't mind being on that committee."

Saul laughed. "Oh, come on, Cooper."

"I'm serious."

"Since when have you cared about urban affairs?" Saul said.

"I care. I care about this city. Of course I care," said Cooper.

"Next time I'll remember that," said Saul, patting him on the shoulder and getting out of his chair.

Cooper remained seated. "You didn't ask me. You didn't ask anyone I know to serve on that committee. You overlooked an entire segment of the population."

Saul turned and looked at him, amazed. "Are you serious?" he said.

"I am, Saul," Cooper said. And suddenly he really was.

"Look, buddy," said Saul. "There are no Chinese people on that committee. And no Greeks. And no Irish. And you could say we overlooked the entire Lithuanian community as well!"

Cooper stood up. "That's not the point. We have a real involvement in that hotel. My grandfather sold the land on which it's built. Lucy Dunbar's great-grandmother danced with presidents there! Bill Satterfield's great uncle was the architect!" He was so agitated that his towel slipped off, and he could feel his pecker nodding frantically in agreement.

The argument was becoming noisy. Other men were turning at their lockers, stopping on their way to the showers, gathering around.

"The committee is already established," said Saul.

"I'm sure it is," said Cooper.

"Do you have anything particular you'd like to contribute to our deliberations?" said Saul.

"Yes I do," said Cooper, thinking of the Snow Ball.

"Then I'll ask the committee if you might come and make your pitch," said Saul.

"Thank you very much," said Cooper.

They got dressed quickly and in silence. As they were walking toward the parking lot, Saul said, "Are we still on for next week?"

"On?"

"Our game."

"Of course we're on. Why wouldn't we be on?" said Cooper. "My territory this time, of course."

"Right," nodded Saul. And then they got into their separate cars and drove home.

4

Kitty Price was the prettiest girl in dancing school, not only in Cooper's class, but right on up through the Junior Assemblies. Everybody knew that. When, on Saturday nights, Mr. Van Dam reached the moment in class when "the young gentlemen will now ask the young ladies to dance," all the boys would dash across the floor and slide into a kind of hockey stop in front of Kitty, checking or shoving each other out of the way.

"Stop!" Mr. Van Dam would bellow, already pounding his cane so rapidly on the floor that it sounded like the machine gun in *The Charge of the Light Brigade.* "Go back! Return! Take your seats! Behave like gentlemen!" And back they'd go, back to sit on the edge of their seats while Kitty would sit demurely opposite them, eyes downcast, smoothing her dress over her knees.

"The first young gentleman will ask the first young lady to dance," Mr. Van Dam would then say wryly. And slowly, one by one, each would walk across the room to stand opposite a seated girl, then bow stiffly, right hand in front, left hand behind, as the girl would rise and curtsy, and then stand facing him. Those times, it would just be luck as to who got Kitty.

"Handkerchiefs out!" Mr. Van Dam would bark, and out of the boys' breast pockets would emerge a row of clean, white, ironed handkerchiefs, each to be placed carefully in the palm of the right hand, that hand then being positioned carefully at the waist of the girl, the handkerchief there, of course, to prevent any actual physical contact between the girl's pristine frock and the boy's foul, tainted, and corrupt male hand.

"Music, Mr. Cromeier, if you please," Mr. Van Dam would then call out, and around they'd go, those strange, ungainly, oddly matched couples, half the girls taller than half the boys, silently counting time with the music, taking large, stiff-legged steps, watching their own feet with grim concentration, blushing, sweating, moving in a slow, grim, mechanical circle around the room, edging as far away as possible from Mr. Van Dam, looking like guilty sinners enduring a perverse punishment in some strange circle of hell.

If you got Kitty, it all felt a little different. And that wasn't simply because she was the prettiest girl there, though she was, with her short bouncy hair, and odd lopsided smile, and firm little legs with feet that pointed outward. It was much more than just her looks that made her so exciting.

In the first place, she wasn't always there. She was absent a lot, and late a lot, so when you got her, you always felt you got something rare and special, like the wishbone or a four-leaf clover. She wasn't the world's greatest dancer—at least not until Jack came along—but she was small, and responsive, and funny. Funny, because she had this casual attitude about the whole thing. She didn't care if she was late, and sometimes she'd duck out early, and when she was dancing there was always a twinkle in her eye which seemed to undercut the solemnity of the occasion.

Cooper would stand in front of her, all stiff and uneasy in his dark blue suit, and bow and do the handkerchief thing, and Kitty would kind of roll her eyes, and make her curtsy look even sillier than it had to be, and then hold out her arms with a sigh, as if to say, "Oh, well, this is a dumb thing we're doing, but let's do it, shall we, rather than make a stink about it." She'd whisper rather cruel little jokes in his ear about the other dancers as they were clumping around, which was funny and sexy at the same time. And if he stepped on her toes, or steered her by mistake into another couple, she'd say "Eeek!" or "Ooof!" or "Egad, sir!" like a character in a comic book, and that was funny, too. Occasionally she'd actually strike up a conversation and keep it going for a while. So dancing school was O.K. when Cooper got Kitty Price to dance with.

O.K. for a while, at least. But after they had circled the ballroom once or twice, he could tell she was getting bored. She'd become just a little late on the moves, just a touch, as if she had to take a fraction of a moment's thought before she followed him. It seemed to be a small hint, a tiny assertion of independence, as if she had to persuade herself that taking the step or making the turn was probably the best thing, or at least the only thing, she could do under the circumstances.

37

And then he'd have to work a little harder to lead her. Other times, he'd notice her looking over his shoulder, glancing around, a little bit distracted, as if she thought she was missing out on someone, or something, somewhere else in the room.

"Hey! Pay attention, Kitty," Cooper said to her once, when she actually stumbled.

"Who, me?" she said, vaguely.

"Yeah, you. Shape up or ship out." He had just learned that expression from *Action in the North Atlantic* that very afternoon.

"Oh sorry," she said. "I was just thinking . . . "

"Don't. It's dangerous."

"No, I mean really. I was thinking what saps we are. Shuffling around like a bunch of zombies. Sometimes I feel like a perfect pill. I mean, what's the *point?*"

But then she'd squeeze his hand, or whisper some crack in his ear, and on they'd dance, until Mr. Van Dam made them change partners or resume their seats while he demonstrated a new step.

Kitty probably was casual about dancing school because she could afford to be. She was the richest girl in town. "Oh, I imagine the Prices have an income of at least a half a million a year," Cooper's father would say. "At least. After taxes." She lived in a huge house on Delaware Avenue, and she'd arrive down at the George Washington Hotel in a big black Packard driven by a chauffeur named Herman who would double-park until she was ready to go home. Cooper used to go to her house for birthday parties when he was little, and they'd all have a great time playing on the built-in elevator, or exploring the innumerable bathrooms, or driving the elec-

38

tric Redbug up and down the long driveway and into the garage, where they had this gigantic turntable just for turning cars around.

Once, when they were playing sardines-in-a-box, and Cooper was hiding with Kitty under the piano in the music room, he asked her to marry him when he grew up.

"I can't," Kitty said. "I'm too rich."

"That's why I want to marry you," Cooper said.

"Well I still can't," she said. "When you're as rich as I am, it has to be someone really special. Which you're not."

Cooper accepted that, and then they were found by the others.

Even Mr. Van Dam treated Kitty Price with unusual deference. It was rather obvious. "Good evening, Miss Price," he'd say with a particularly oily bow when she came through the receiving line, though he normally wouldn't bother with other people's names. He never reprimanded her when she was whispering, and he never singled her out when she made a mistake, and he never let her be left without a partner. He needed her there. Without her, his whole enterprise might have been in trouble. Her diffident behavior, her latenesses, her more than occasional absences must have frightened him considerably.

"Where is Miss Price?" he'd say, when she wasn't there. "Has anyone seen Miss Price? She's not ill, I hope. We would like to assume that she has a more pressing engagement." Dancing school without Kitty Price wouldn't have lasted very long. He knew that. Probably Kitty knew it, too, in her bones, which made her all the more exciting to dance with.

Of course Cooper didn't know it at all. All he knew was that he had to go. A world without dancing school was unimaginable to him. It was simply there, to be gone to, to be endured, to be gotten through, like diphtheria shots or the ablative absolute. And Mr. Van Dam was simply one of those ageless and unavoidable figures who marked his life like Charlie the Barber, or Doctor Riddle who made you strip even if you just had a cold, or old Miss Connery down at the Franklin School who had taught him, and his father, and his mother, and his sister, how to factor with two unknowns.

In any case, Kitty went through her paces in a more casual way than the rest of them, and they simply thought that that's what it meant to be rich. She wouldn't show up if the ice-skating in Delaware Park had been particularly good, or if her parents took her to Lake Placid to ski, or if she wanted to hear an especially exciting segment of "I Love a Mystery" on the radio. She'd be late if her chauffeur had to do an errand for her mother, and she'd leave early if her father appeared in the visitor's section, glowering impatiently, looking at his watch. She was even late for the Cotillion at the end of the year, and left right after the ice cream. She moved in and out of dancing school with a wink and a shrug, which made everyone else's struggles to be punctual, to be neat, to be polite, to dance gracefully seem all the more hectic and contorted.

Then Jack came into the picture, and made it a very different story.

5

Cooper's next squash game with Saul Radner, in court number four at the Buffalo Tennis and Squash Club, wasn't much fun at all. The deal was that they'd play their squash, have their beers, and then Cooper would come over to Saul's house for a bite with him and Judy, because the Downtown Rehabilitation Committee would be meeting right there at eight o'clock. Cooper could make his case, whatever it might be, to them then. That's what they arranged over the telephone, briskly and efficiently, but that's not quite the way it worked out.

The squash was extremely unpleasant. They walked into the court loaded for bear, and they let each other have it. Every point was bitterly contested. Saul barged and thrashed around the small white box like an imprisoned animal. Cooper scampered and flailed. It was the rapier versus the

41

mace. Twice Cooper hit Saul on the back of his legs with the ball, once purposely. Three times, Saul caught Cooper in the wide arc of his swing, and three times it hurt like hell. There were arguments all through the game about foot faults, about lets, about the score. Buff Thurston, who was upstairs in the bar having his martini, heard the noise and came to the window to watch, and finally felt compelled to open the casement and call down: "Hey, take it easy, you guys! You're going to kill yourselves! Seriously!"

They never finished. Cooper turned his ankle going after what he thought was a really cheap, dinky corner shot, and Saul already had the beginnings of a bloody nose, so they agreed to call it a day. "How'd it go, fellas?" said Gary Strake, when they staggered into the locker room, but neither of them answered. They undressed and took their showers in silence. Bill, the steward, automatically brought them their Heinekens afterwards, but they didn't even say thank you. They sat uneasily on the edge of the leather chairs and stared at the limp jockstraps and soaked T-shirts crumpled on the floor in front of them.

"The thing is, Saul," said Cooper, finally, "squash is a very civilized game. It was developed by the English. You're supposed to pound the ball, all right, but you're also supposed to get out of the way so the other guy can pound it. When that goes, the whole thing goes."

"I didn't get out of the way?" said Saul. "Seems to me all I was doing was trying to get out of the way."

"Maybe we'd better not discuss it," said Cooper, waving away Bill who was bringing them their second beers.

They got up and started to get dressed.

"Hey, lookit," said Cooper, as he was tying his tie, "I'd better not come over for dinner tonight after all, O.K.? I ought to have dinner with Liz. Is that O.K.? I'll come over afterwards and talk to the committee. O.K.?"

"Fine," said Saul.

"Liz has been out a lot at night. So I really ought to go home and touch base. O.K.?"

"I said fine," said Saul. He gathered up his stuff and left.

Cooper put his things in his locker, and then combed his hair. Gary Strake was standing in front of the mirror, powdering and spraying his plump body.

"He looked sore," said Gary. "Did you beat him?"

"No," said Cooper.

"The thing about those guys is they'll do anything to win. I have to deal with them in business, and I know."

"That wasn't it, Gary," said Cooper. "It's much more complicated than that." And he walked out of the club.

Actually, Liz had a meeting that night too, so she was eating at the hospital, where she worked. Cooper warmed up some old meat loaf and peas from the icebox (now that the last child had left for college there wasn't much to choose from) and telephoned Lucy Dunbar while he ate.

"Hey, I thought you were over at Saul Radner's, defending the faith," she said. "I thought this was the big night."

"It is. I'm going over in a while," Cooper said. "I just wanted to recharge my batteries."

"You sound a little low, Cooper."

"I don't know. What am I doing? What am I arguing for? Some dumb dance . . ."

"Cooper! Cooper, now don't flag! That's the trouble with us these days. We back off, we give up, we retreat into our little shells. That's what I've been doing since my divorce, and it's gotten me nowhere. Now let's seize the hour! I've spoken to a number of people about this, and they all think it's a wonderful idea. Bringing back the Snow Ball. It's symbolic, Cooper! It puts us back on the map! Now if you won't go over there and make the case, I'll do it myself. I mean it. I'll call Saul Radner right now and tell him I'm on my way! Honestly! It's indicative, it's just indicative of how things are in this town that you'd get cold feet at the last minute."

"I'll do it, Lucy. I said I'd do it, and I will."

"Then do it with conviction. Think of the fun we'll have. Think of everyone getting together. Think of that lovely ballroom used the way it should be used for the first time in at least twenty years. Think of Jack and Kitty."

"We don't have Jack and Kitty, Lucy."

"We can *get* them, Cooper. I know we can get them if we can just get the Snow Ball!"

"O.K., O.K."

"Have I recharged your batteries. Or not?"

"You've recharged them, Lucy," Cooper said with a slight sigh.

"Good. Then call me afterwards. I don't care how late it is. I want to know the outcome."

The Radners lived in a large, rather dark Tudor house on the other side of the park. Both Saul and Judy met Cooper at the door. They were unusually polite and solicitous about his coat, and there was no mention of either the game that afternoon or the fact that he hadn't come to dinner. They led him into the living room where the committee was already convened, drinking coffee and eating large chunks of cake, made, Judy said, by her housekeeper that very afternoon. Everyone got up to meet Cooper, and they all shook hands.

Saul had told the committee that Cooper wanted to make a proposal, so they settled down to listen. Angela Montini brushed a few cake crumbs off her bosom and took time to admire its obvious amplitude before she folded her hands in her lap and smiled. Tad Kowalski lit a cigarette and tried to look like Lech Walesa. Arthur Johnson, M.D., who was considered one of the best gastroenterologists east of Delaware Avenue, furtively popped a Rolaids in his mouth. Judy Radner pulled up a chair slightly outside the circle and stayed to listen. Saul sat in his reading chair, with *Commentary* still on the table beside him, and waited.

Cooper spoke. Cooper spoke well. His father had been a wonderful after-dinner speaker, and those old genes rose to the occasion now. He apologized for taking the committee's time, and appreciated the fact that they must already be well into their deliberations. But he wanted to say, it "behooved him" to say, that they may have overlooked something important. There they were, planning to celebrate the rebirth of downtown Buffalo, hoping to center their celebrations in the magnificent old George Washington Hotel, and yet ignoring the crowning jewel of that edifice, its Grand Ballroom on the second floor.

"Ballrooms were designed for balls," Cooper said, though that didn't sound quite right. "Ballrooms were designed to be danced in. I hope I'm not delegating myself to the dark ages when I say that I have danced in that room many times. I know how it comes to life when an orchestra is playing, the sconces and chandeliers are lit, and myriad couples are whirling over the floor, that special floor which was specially laid over a hundred years ago, just to be danced on!"

Indeed, he went on, there had once been an annual festivity which displayed the room and those who danced in it in all their glory: the Snow Ball, Buffalo's own Snow Ball, famous throughout the Eastern Seaboard. He had been there. He knew. It had occurred the Friday after Christmas, just when they were planning their own event, and so why not revive it? What better way to celebrate the city than to resuscitate the Snow Ball?

He concluded with a richly democratic vision. He called on all his old humanities courses from Brown. He talked about dance as the ultimate expression of human community, beyond the separating effects of language, culture, and class. He saw this as a chance to bring together all the disparate elements of the city in a great, swirling circle of movement. Here in this elegant old room, Jew would link arms with black, Pole with Italian, Wasp with—Lithuanian (and he glanced at Saul). His eyes watered as he spoke. His tongue waxed eloquent. He was really rather effective.

He finished and sat down. There was silence.

"Would anyone like more coffee?" Judy Radner asked brightly.

Nobody did. There was more silence.

"Dance, huh," said Ted Kowalski, lighting another cigarette. "You mean, wear tuxes and stuff? Like a wedding?"

"I have a hostess gown," said Angela.

"I think dress should be optional," said Cooper magnanimously.

Tad looked at him peculiarly. There was a return to silence.

Finally, Saul spoke. "I think we should probably share with

Cooper some of the things we've been talking about," he said. And he took a stuffed manila folder out of his briefcase and shuffled through it. To begin with, he said, they hadn't planned to use the ballroom at all.

"Not at *all?*" said Cooper.

"Not at all," said Saul. They felt it was too formal and prepossessing. They planned to use the main floor of the hotel only, the lobby and the foyer, both of which were being extensively remodeled and "opened up" under the new redevelopment program. The ballroom had been left pretty much as it was, and would be used in the future for banquets and wedding receptions, but they didn't see any need for it on Winterfest, which was supposed to commemorate a new and revitalized downtown.

"I see," said Cooper.

"Actually, we're not as far apart as you'd think," said Saul. What they planned to do was to divide the large, recently expanded downstairs lobby into a series of ethnic or cultural areas, where the many and diverse qualities of the city could be variously displayed. Ticket holders, or rather "guests," would be able to stroll from booth to boutique, now stopping to "purchase" a native artifact—a Mexican bead necklace, a Nigerian wood carving—and now sampling a morsel of portable food—a Greek kabob, a Chinese spare rib, a Polish sausage in a French croissant.

There would be educational booths as well, Saul said. The Historical Society had offered to set up a display presenting the growth of the city, beginning with Indian dioramas, models of the old forts, the early farm village, and the coming of industry. Next to it, the Science Museum had proposed a slide show on the City of Tomorrow, with population projections, architectural sketches of condominium complexes and shopping malls, and a row of nonviolent video games to help occupy the kids. The Millard Fillmore Hospital planned to provide a Health Corner, where they'd take your blood pressure and offer preliminary training in Cardiac Pulmonary Resuscitation. The Christian Scientists and the Mormons had asked for tables side by side, and the Anti-Smoking League had insisted on a roped off area all to itself. The Sierra Club had proposed a booth on dioxin and nuclear disarmament, and the Jewish Community Center had proposed a display on the Holocaust, though the committee had tactfully talked them out of that.

"It all sounds very nice," said Cooper.

"I'm not finished yet," said Saul, and went on. These booths and displays would circle the lobby, while in the more open areas there would be plenty of chairs and benches —"conversation areas"—where people might cluster and discuss what they had viewed, and bought, and eaten. Furthermore, in alcoves at either end of the lobby, there would be a series of performances and entertainments at intervals throughout the evening. There would be, for example, string quartets played by the best musicians in the Philharmonic, and because Saul had a niece who was studying the cello in New York, she might be playing too. There would be Gospel singers from the Abyssinian Baptist Church, courtesy of Doctor Johnson's brother, who was a part-time pastor there. There would be duets and trios from Verdi and Donizetti sung by students from Ignatius Loyola College, where Angela Montini had spent some of her happiest years. There would be an exhibition of Silesian folk dancing led by Tad Kowalski's wife and their three daughters, all dressed in

48

peasant garb. And finally, so the young people wouldn't become restless, there would be a short concert late in the evening—"about eleven or thereabouts"—by the Rebels, who were generally acknowledged to be the most exciting punk rock group in town.

"People can dance *then*, Cooper," said Judy Radner, reassuringly. "If they want to."

"Sure," said Saul, closing his manila folder and tapping its stuffed contents back into shape. "Anyway, you can see what we've been up to." They all looked at Cooper, as if for applause.

"It sounds very nice," he said, getting up. "Thank you very much for telling me." He began to shake hands all around. "And thank you for listening to my own suggestions." He was on automatic pilot now, going through the motions, motions which it occurred to him he probably had acquired in dancing school. "Thank you. Good to meet you. Thank you very much." He even called people by name.

Saul and Judy accompanied him to the door, and Saul helped him on with his coat.

"You see, Cooper?" Saul said, patting him on the back. "You see why you're not on the committee? This is all very eighties and ethnocentric, Cooper. This is all about the old country."

"I see. Yes. Thank you," said Cooper, shaking hands. "Thank you, Judy, for that delicious cake." He gave her a perfunctory kiss on the cheek. "Thank you both very much." And he left.

But as he drove home, he thought, "Goddammit, I come from an old country, too! We had our costumes and customs and convictions, and it's high time we trotted them out!"

49

The ballroom was free that night. They could still have the Snow Ball on their own. Why the hell not? They'd bang the drum, and pass the hat, and get everyone to come out of the woodwork, and have one hell of a blast, just like the old days. Maybe he hadn't convinced anyone on the Downtown Rehabilitation Committee with his speech, but he had convinced himself! And that was without even considering Kitty and Jack!

6

Jack Daley joined Cooper's class in dancing school halfway through the second year. He looked vaguely familiar, but nobody could quite pin down who he was. He didn't go to Nichols School, and he hadn't been to Elmwood or Franklin before that, and he wore light blue socks for the first two weeks he was there until Fritzie Klinger made a crack about them. Still, there he was, from January on, waiting in the men's cloak room, always the first to arrive, usually doing his homework, hunkered down in a corner reading a battered, secondhand textbook entitled *Our American Democracy*.

One time, when Jack had been there about a month, Binkie Byers grabbed the book out of his hands and read inside the cover: "Property of Holy Angels Collegiate Institute."

"*Holy Angels Collegiate Institute?* Je-zus. Where the hell is *that?*" Binkie asked, to no one in particular.

51

"I think it's over on the west side," said somebody else.

Jack by this time was on his feet. "Give me that," he said to Binkie.

"Make me," said Binkie.

Jack didn't even hit him. He just gave him a big shove, which sent him reeling into the overcoats and set all the extra metal hangers rattling on the rack.

"O.K., O.K., O.K.," Binkie said, quickly handing back the book. "I can't fight anyway. I got my good clothes on."

"Hmmm," said someone, and that was that. Jack went back to his corner to do his homework, and the other boys started milling around, and soon Mrs. Van Dam stuck her head in the doorway and clapped her hands and said, "All right, boys." And they lined up to march up to dance.

Cooper Jones got to know Jack strictly by luck. There had been a mix-up in the carpool, so his mother had driven him down to the hotel, but they had a dinner party that night, so she couldn't bring him home. "You'll just have to take the bus," she said, giving him fifteen cents carfare. "You're a big boy now."

So after dancing school, Cooper slouched grumpily over to the bus stop, and who was already waiting there but Jack, studying his civics under the streetlight. They got to talking and discovered they saw eye to eye on a number of issues: the batting stance of Mel Ott, the decline of "The Shadow," and the basic superiority of the Curtiss-Wright P-40 over the Bell Aerocobra.

Now another lucky thing was that Cooper's grandfather had given him a crisp new five dollar bill that very afternoon just for stopping by and saying hello after the movies. "Don't let it burn a hole in your pocket," his grandfather had said, but Cooper had it with him, and he felt rich and generous.

And hungry, after all that dancing. So he asked Jack to walk up to Smither's with him for a chocolate ice cream soda.

"I'm flush. Get whatever you want," Cooper said. "Within reason," he added, imitating his grandfather.

They settled down at the old marble-topped counter, and ordered their sodas, and watched the sodajerk squirt in the fizz, and spun their stools a few times, and made paper snakes out of their straw covers, and looked at the new Coca-Cola ads; and when their sodas came, they began to make even more conversation.

"I liked it tonight when we started learning the waltz," Jack said, between the gurgling noises they were now making with their straws.

"You *liked* it?"

"Sure. I like it even better than the fox trot. You can cover more ground."

"You mean you *like* dancing school?" Cooper said.

"Sure."

"No kidding."

"I'm paying for it myself," Jack said.

"You're *paying* for *dancing* school? With your own *money?*"

"Sure."

"How *come?*"

"Because I wanted to go."

Cooper thought Jack was pulling his leg, so he laughed and shook his head.

"I'm serious," Jack said. He was digging with his spoon for the last of the ice cream at the bottom of his glass. "By the way, don't I look familiar?"

Cooper looked at him. "Sort of," he said. He knew he had seen him before.

Jack slid off his stool, handed Cooper his jacket, and went

to the door of the drugstore, which he opened with a flourish for a lady coming in.

"Thank you, sonny," she said.

Jack returned to the counter. "*Now* do I look familiar?" he said.

Cooper got it. "You were one of the bellboys!" he said. "You were one of those kids hanging around the lobby!"

"Right. I carried bags, turned the revolving door, and last year I handled the cookies for your spring party."

"The *Cotillion?*" Cooper said. "You were at the Cotillion?"

"I did the cookies," said Jack, miming with his hands, and now Cooper saw him standing behind the table in a white jacket and black bow tie, serving cookies with silver tongs as people came down the line.

"My dad knows the hotel manager," Jack said. "I got the job weekends for sixty-seven cents an hour. I'd watch you guys come in, and sometimes I'd sneak away and come up to the ballroom and watch what you were doing through a crack in the door."

"What door where?" said Cooper, a little mad because someone had been peeking.

"The one behind the guy on the piano. It leads to the kitchen."

Cooper had never noticed that door.

"Well, it's there," said Jack. "You can see a lot from it. I learned all the basic steps just by watching. I practiced when I got home. That's how come I could start in the middle of the second year."

"But how come you *want* to?" Cooper asked, amazed. He thought it would be much more exciting just to work, to

54

have a job, particularly in the hotel, eating as many cookies as you wanted, carrying trays and bags, getting tips for doing it, building up your biceps even while you were stashing away sixty-seven cents an hour. "I mean, why go to *dancing* school? Jesus, and *pay* for it!"

Jack pushed away his glass and wiped his mouth with his napkin. "Three reasons," he said, holding up three fingers and looking at Cooper very directly. "First, it looks good."

"Looks good?"

"I mean you look good when you're doing it."

"Tell me another."

"I mean you *can*. If you do it well. And I intend to do it well."

"What's the second reason?" asked Cooper.

"The girls. The girls look good."

"*Those* girls? In *dancing school?*"

"Some of them are knockouts, in my opinion," said Jack determinedly. "Some of them are real queens."

"What's the third thing?" asked Cooper.

Jack looked at him very seriously, very directly, with a totally focused gaze. "Dancing school will be good for my future," he said.

"Your future?"

"My career. Getting to know you people will help me succeed in life."

Cooper was very much aware of Jack's blue eyes as they bore into his own. He'd never paid much attention to people's eyes before, but he noticed these, all right. They were so direct that he couldn't help but look away.

"I guess you're right," Cooper said.

55

"Oh, sure," said Jack. "I was supposed to put the money away for my college education, but I decided this was an equally important investment."

Cooper nodded solemnly and finished the dregs of his soda. He had intended to make all sorts of weird noises with his straw, but now he thought better of it. Because after all, Jack was right. Dancing school *was* filled with important people. His own father had real estate signs all over the city and was on the board of Nichols School. Binkie Byer's father ran some bank. Kitty Price's family was terribly rich from a number of sources and was said to own stock in *Life* and *Time*. Oh, sure. They all were terribly important when you came right down to it. The only hitch was, he wondered whether his father could have gotten him a weekend job as a bellboy at the George Washington Hotel.

The drugstore was closing and it was time to leave. Cooper felt important enough to leave a ten cent tip for the soda jerk, even though they had been sitting at the counter rather than at a table. Jack thanked him for the soda, and Cooper said, "Not at all. My pleasure," and then he ran for his bus, since Jack had to take a different one to get home.

The next week, Cooper told his mother he didn't need to be in the carpool anymore. He would take the bus down and back. His mother worried that he might get beaten up by those Italian boys from Black Rock if they saw him walking home in his new camel's hair overcoat, but he insisted she let him do it. And so he began to have a soda regularly with Jack after dancing school.

Jack told him a lot of things he never knew before. For instance, Jack told him how tough it was to get into dancing school. Cooper had just assumed that anyone could go whose parents wanted him to, but now he learned that wasn't the case at all. Last year, after the last class, Jack had changed out of his bellboy's uniform and gone up to Mr. Van Dam and asked if he could join the class, and Mr. Van Dam had said, no, definitely not, he was sorry, the class was full.

"Which was a lie," said Jack, "because I saw there were extra girls every week, so I knew they needed boys."

"So how did you get in?" Cooper asked.

Well, it was complicated. He got his father to speak to Bill Cassidy when they went out for a smoke during the sermon at Mass. And Bill Cassidy spoke to his sister, who had married a Haskell and lived over by the park. And Mrs. Haskell worked with Mrs. Denny as a Gray Lady in the hospital. And Mrs. Denny was a good friend of Mrs. Foster.

"Mrs. Foster is the Queen Bee of the whole operation," said Jack. "She doesn't just stand there next to Van Dam and shake hands. She makes up lists! And Mrs. Denny got her to put me on it."

(Cooper asked his mother later about it. "That's true, darling," she said. "Poor Mrs. Foster's husband died and didn't leave her much money. So that's what she does. She organizes things. She guards the gates a little.")

Anyway, finally, halfway into the next year, an invitation for dancing school arrived at Jack's house. He signed up, and sent in his money order for $450.00.

"Four hundred and fifty *dollars?*" said Cooper. "Is that what it *costs?* To go to *dancing* school?"

"Plus fifteen dollars extra for the Cotillion at the end of the year," said Jack. So even the money he made as a bellhop wasn't enough. He had to borrow from his uncle to make it up. And next year, at Junior Assemblies, he'd have to pay even more, because Mr. Cromeier brought in a violinist and an accordion player, and that was put on the bill.

"That's O.K.," said Jack. "I can swing it. I'll work this summer. My dad knows guys in construction, so I should make a pile."

The lucky stiff, Cooper thought. Working in construction. Out in the sun. Building himself up. Learning dirty jokes from the workers. Making all that dough. Think of the Victrola records you could buy with that dough. Think of the bike. While poor Cooper had to settle for rolling the community tennis courts over in Canada for the third year in a row at ten dollars a week. And be tutored in French by some guy who couldn't even get into the war.

"I think it's your turn to pay for the sodas this week," he said to Jack when the check came.

"Right," said Jack, and it cost him more, too, since this week they both had ordered extra scoops of vanilla ice cream.

And so Jack Daley came to dancing school—"That nice-looking Irish boy from the west side," the mothers began to say—and he looked good from the beginning. There was a kind of dash and charm to him, even as he offered his arm to a girl on the opening march up the stairs to the ballroom, and you could tell he'd be a good dancer, almost from the springy way he walked.

Of course, Mr. Van Dam didn't like him much. You could tell that, too. He obviously thought he was an interloper, a Johnny-Come-Lately, so he looked away from him in the receiving line, and never complimented him or called him by name. But he didn't pick on him, either. Jack was too good for that. He was always there, and always on time, and studied his civics quietly in the cloakroom, and learned his steps, and did what he was told, and never dashed across the floor to get to Kitty. He seemed glad to dance with anyone he was paired with, and could do the rumba and the Viennese waltz and the schottische and the Lambeth walk better than anyone else.

And soon, after dancing school, while the girls still went home in carpools, and Kitty went home in her chauffeur-driven Packard, the other boys began to follow Cooper and Jack to Smither's for an ice cream soda. First they settled like starlings in a noisy row along the counter. Then, as more came, they moved to one of the marble-topped tables. Finally there were so many that they had to push several tables together. Mr. Smither was nervous about having so many of them hanging around that late in his store. He had visions of them shooting the paper coverings from their straws all over the place, and making wisecracks to him ("Have you got Prince Albert in the can?") or to the patrons ("Run to the roundhouse, lady, we'll never corner you there!"), or swiping comic books from the rack as they left.

But they did none of these things. Jack kept them in line. He held them entranced with his tales of the world west of Richmond Avenue: Holy Angels Collegiate Institute, where the classes were taught by cruel priests and arbitrary nuns; Saint Teresa's Church, where beautiful Italian girls lined up every Friday night to confess deep and mysterious sins; the Fourteenth Ward, where the political life of the city was determined by fat cats in the back rooms of bars and bowling

7

"Well, I see you've gotten the ball rolling," said Cooper's wife Liz one morning in the kitchen as they were getting breakfast before they both went off to work. The newspaper had arrived in time, for once, and she had discovered a small article in the back section:

SNOW BALL CONTEMPLATED

A group of interested citizens are hoping to revive the traditional Snow Ball in the Grand Ballroom of the George Washington Hotel this December. The affair would celebrate the reopening of the hotel and would take place concurrently with the city's Winterfest, organized by the Downtown Rehabilitation Committee. When asked whether the festivities might conflict, Mr. Saul Radner, chairman of the Committee, replied, "We're a democracy, aren't we? And it's the holiday season. Let a thousand flowers bloom."

"Lucy Dunbar must have called the paper," said Cooper.

"Apparently," said Liz. "And I hear you've done some telephoning, too. Down at the office."

"I've called a few people. Sure. Just to see if they were interested."

"Oh, Cooper."

"What's wrong with that?"

"The Snow Ball? Dragging that old thing out of moth balls?"

"Why not? It could be fun."

"It could be a complete and total disaster."

"That's why I haven't mentioned it, Liz. Because you're always so goddam negative about these things."

"I'm negative about that, Cooper. I don't even have an *evening* dress anymore."

He munched his granola. She concentrated on her egg.

"I also heard, through the grapevine, that you're actually thinking of asking Jack and Kitty," Liz said, after a moment.

"We might. If we can get things going."

"That's the silliest thing I ever heard."

"Why do you say that?"

"Because they probably haven't even *seen* each other in thirty years. Much less danced."

"All the more exciting."

"Oh, Cooper. Honestly! Jack is where? Tied up in politics out in Indiana or somewhere. And who knows where Kitty ended up?"

"She's in Florida. I checked."

"Well, there you are," said Liz, downing her coffee and jamming her cup into the dishwasher. "It's over, Cooper. It's all over. The whole thing. And probably just as well. Now stop trying to dig up a dead dog."

"Jesus, Liz, you have such a delicate way of putting things."

"Well, I just think there are more important things in the world than the Snow Ball," she said. "Now check the stove and turn down the heat. I'm late." She grabbed her briefcase and was gone, slamming the front door, then slamming the door of the old station wagon, starting the engine with a noisy roar, then off and away.

She was a social worker at the Meyer Memorial Hospital, eight-thirty to four-thirty, Monday through Friday. She had gone back to school after the children hit their teens, and had gotten her master's out at the university. Her specialty was family therapy and her title was "Interventionist." Her job was to intervene. When children were mistreated or wives beaten up or husbands hopelessly betrayed, there would be Liz, intervening. And when she wasn't doing that, she was intervening on a larger scale. She was on the Buffalo Fair Housing Committee and intervened when landlords were suspected of not renting to blacks. She was on an education task force and intervened in the School Committee hearings on behalf of sex education. She marched on Washington twice, to intervene on behalf of civil rights, and against the Vietnam War. When people smoked in restaurants, Liz intervened. When they talked in movies, when they had more than eight items in the speed check-out line at the supermarket, when they neglected to pick up on the street after their dogs, Liz would intervene. She was never rude or indignant; she was always quietly firm. But she was always there, intervening. Once, on a vacation, they found themselves sitting on a plane which couldn't take off because it had been oversold. Two anguished passengers were struggling over a single seat.

"Perhaps I could intervene here," said Liz, marching up the aisle, and before Cooper knew it, she had solved the difficulty by offering their own seats to solve the problem. They had had to sit in the Pittsburgh airport for two hours waiting for the next plane, but Liz had beautifully intervened.

"Liz has bloomed," Cooper's friends would say, or rather his female friends. "You must be terribly proud."

"I am, I am," Cooper would say. And he was. Sort of. But their lives had changed considerably. They couldn't get away much in the summer now, for example. Liz's job precluded that. And they couldn't really entertain much, because Liz put in a long day and normally needed the weekend to catch up on the laundry, the shopping, whatever. And she had pretty well given up tennis, so there went those pleasant Sunday afternoons playing mixed doubles with the Randalls or the McKees. She still liked to go to the movies now and then, but not so much, and when she did go likely as not she was so tired she'd fall asleep.

Oh, there were good things, too, that had happened in their lives as a result of her new career. He'd learned how to cook, for example. A little. A few things. Chicken. Brown rice. Broccoli. And gardening. He'd gotten into that. The garden looked pretty good these days. When they sold the house, which they were planning to do, the garden would help the price considerably.

So all that was to the good. They'd both learned things. He'd gotten his hands dirty, so to speak, and she'd opened up her mind. They both lived brisk, active, independent lives. If Liz didn't want to go to a party, he'd go without her, and there were no raised eyebrows or solicitous looks. And if Liz had to go to a social workers conference or interventionists seminar in Dallas or Seattle, off she went and that was fine, too. He missed her, of course, and she missed him, but life went on, and they survived without each other.

In fact, they seemed to survive sometimes on separateness. They almost cultivated it. Look at the way they had breakfast, for example. They bustled from refrigerator to toaster to coffeemaker in a series of separate stops. They had separate things. Cooper insisted on his granola, while Liz demanded her egg. Cooper made tea, Liz brewed coffee. They even had separate newspapers, so they wouldn't fight. And they didn't sit down much. They stood, each at his or her corner of the counter reading, sipping, munching, occasionally commenting on the news, before they went off to their separate jobs. They prided themselves on their differences.

They made an effort to get together for the evening meal, though. They both tried to be home for that. They'd try to prepare the meal together, and at least put place mats on the kitchen table, and take their time over their food. But here again, there was some strain. Liz wasn't terribly interested in what Cooper had to tell her about the world of Buffalo real estate, and Cooper had equal difficulty concentrating on Liz's various cases or the politics over at Meyer Memorial.

It was odd. You'd think they'd have a lot to say to each other. It's always interesting who buys what house and how much they paid for it, and Liz's lurid accounts of tormented families would have engaged millions of readers of tabloid newspapers. Yet apparently Cooper and Liz didn't want to hear those things from each other. It was hard to know what they wanted to hear. In any case, they tried hard to pay attention, to ask the right questions, to keep the ball in the air, even though their hearts weren't in it. Sometimes they'd give up, and guiltily lug in the TV to watch the MacNeil-Lehrer Report while Cooper had dessert and Liz didn't.

Things were fine when they discussed the children. They could go all night on that topic. They had three—two boys and a girl—and they discussed them animatedly whenever they could. But these days, how much was there to say? The children no longer brought the delights of infancy, the surprises of childhood, the agonies of adolescence. Both boys were working out west now, and from what Cooper and Liz could tell from their occasional telephone calls, they were happy and well. Their daughter was still in college, but was never there when they tried to call her. It was hard to know what she was up to, or to discuss it.

Cooper tucked his breakfast dishes into the dishwasher, checked the stove, wiped the counter, and wandered into the front hall to adjust the thermostat, since no one would be home all day long. He could hear the furnace cranking doggedly away below him in the cellar, and an occasional radiator sighing sadly upstairs. They had lived in this old house for over twenty years and kept it going primarily for the children: its long lawn so the boys could play ball, its driveway for the tricycles and roller skating and street hockey, its lovely light bedrooms with the beds always made so the kids could always come home. Occasionally he had visions of a sumptuous wedding tent in his garden, flags fluttering like Camelot, under which he would toast his sons and dance with his daughter before passing them on to an attractive, deferential bride or groom. Or else he'd dream of troops of wide-eyed grandchildren, following him adoringly around while he set up the croquet.

But these dreams happened less and less. Both his boys were happily ensconced with what Liz liked to call "spouse-equivalents," and he had the feeling his daughter was, too, which was probably why they never could reach her at the dorm. ("Oh, gosh, she's at the library, Mr. Jones," the room-mate would say. "You just missed her.") None of his children talked much about getting married, and less about having babies, and when they came home last Christmas and he asked them how they'd feel if he sold the house, they shrugged, and looked at each other, and said, "It's your decision, Dad," and started eyeing the furniture.

And of course Liz was eager to sell and get something smaller, more efficient, easier to keep up.

"An apartment?" he'd say. "You want to put me in a *cage?*"

"A *garden* apartment, Cooper. A row house. A con-dominium. *Something.*"

"Over my dead body."

"We just rattle around here now. Poor Eileen is getting too old to clean. It costs us twenty-five dollars just to get the driveway plowed. Let another family have it. Let other children grow up in it. Let it go, Cooper, for God's sake!"

He turned the heat down to fifty-five, keyed in the burglar alarm, and locked the door. Out of impulse, he took a walk around his house. The snow was beginning to go now, and the ground was soft. He had to make his way carefully. On the southern side, hugging the foundation, a few crocuses winked at him brightly. The scylla was already showing up on the patches of lawn. The lilac buds were beginning to bulge. Spring. Soon he'd be raking the leaves out of the flower beds, uncovering the soft green shoots from the bulbs.

Then he'd be taking down the storm windows, teetering on top of a ladder, trying to get a purchase on the rusty old screws, easing the heavy wooden frames down to the ground. Then the liming of the lawn, the planting of the annuals, the planting of the vegetables, the weeding, the mowing, the staking, the pruning, the spraying. And then fall. The storm windows. The gutters. And the leaves. The endless leaves.

"Get a man to do these things," Liz would say. "Get a service. Get a high-school student to at least help." But he couldn't. This house was like an old ship. You couldn't just bring anyone in to sail her. It had taken twenty years to learn. You had to know where the bulbs were, so you could spade around them. You had to know how to ease a storm window onto the sill. You had to care enough to rake a lawn, not simply fan the leaves with a noisy blower. Raking stimulates the roots, aerates the soil, removes the dead grass, something, anyway, you had to rake it. By hand.

And if he got high-school kids in to help, he knew he'd get depressed because they'd simply remind him of his own, and those great old Saturdays and Sundays when everyone pitched in, everyone helped, even Liz, if she wasn't studying, and they'd establish an assembly line washing the storm windows or bagging the leaves, or in the old days raking them all into one huge pile. Then, when they were younger, he'd throw the kids in, one by one, and then the dog, and then even the cat, until there would be this great squealing, heaving turmoil of life under the dead leaves.

Oh, the children, the children. Sometimes his throat would catch and his eyes would water when he talked about them with friends, or even with Liz. "They're not *dead*, Cooper," Liz would say. "Honestly! Now let me get back at these statistics. I've got a staff meeting tomorrow."

No, they weren't dead. They were very much alive, and they'd come home, too, now and then, "sometimes too much," Cooper would say to his friends, half-seriously, after they'd arrived in the middle of a meal, in the middle of the night, lugging their laundry in bulging plastic bags, breaking the washing machine, leaving the milk out, bringing with them various companions of various sexes, sleeping till noon, messing up their rooms, blasting him out of the living room with their stereos and tape decks and extra speakers, until finally he'd explode, yell, there'd be a scene, a discussion, an understanding, a hug, and then suddenly, time for them to go—a frantic drive to a grungy bus station or else some strange, dangerous-looking car honking in the driveway— and then good-bye, good-bye, here's money, drive carefully, work hard, stay well, so long, so long, write, call, good-bye, and he'd feel worse than if they'd never come home at all.

Cooper stood by the garage and looked at his dark, cold house. He remembered how it seemed to throb with excitement when he drove into the driveway after work. He'd come into the kitchen to find the kids cooing over their supper, Liz bustling at the stove, the puppy peeing with excitement. Or later, when he and Liz would come home after a Saturday night party, there it would be, a great, comfortable ark, ablaze with light in a dark world, and then they'd go in to find the children curled comfortably around the TV.

"What's this?" he'd say, half drunk, hugging them, shoving them off to bed. "Are we living in a showboat? Are we paying to light up the entire city of Buffalo?"

Oh, God, the kids. Cooper thought of them as he drove to work. "You have great kids," people would say. "You and Liz have done a bang-up job on those kids." And they had, dammit. They'd been together on that, right on down the line. Through every decision, every crisis, they had seen pretty much eye to eye. "Can I have my ear lobes punctured?" An immediate and common "No." "Do I have to wear a tie to Gramma's?" A similar "Yes." "Why do I have to be home at eleven-thirty?" "Never mind. You just do." Complete and total harmony, treble and bass.

"Of course you have a common background. That's the point. That helps immeasurably in bringing up children," his mother used to say. And she was probably right. He'd met Liz in dancing school, after all. They'd learned the same steps at the same time. They'd gone on to similar prep schools, similar colleges. Their parents had known each other for years. When they became engaged, they agreed completely on the various patterns for their various dinner plates, which were to be made available at Pitt Petri's and The Savoy Shop down on Delaware Avenue. They inherited the same sort of furniture, were used to the same sort of food, went on their honeymoon to the same place in Bermuda where both sets of parents had gone before them.

And so it had all worked out beautifully with their children. They provided a solid, confident base of commonly held customs and values, a taut, firm net of love and support, from which their children could jump, and on which they could land when they fell.

"You make us sound like a trampoline," Liz said to Cooper when she heard him describing it this way. But trampoline or not, they both knew it was true. They were good parents, and they knew it, and they loved each other most when they were most conscious of it. Sitting together during the school plays, the music recitals, the games, the graduations, they

70

would hold hands and feel deep shivers of delight in each other and in what they had made together, and that would make them want to celebrate themselves in the great, wide, inherited double bed, where these fabulous offspring had once been conceived.

Cooper drove his car up the ramp of the new parking facility near his office and walked across the mall to the Ellicott Square Building, where he would settle in at his father's old desk.

He knew what his father would say about all this, if he were still alive. "Hold on," he'd say. "Hold onto your house and your lovely wife and those fine bright children. Hold onto those stocks I left you. Don't let anything go."

Well, he'd already sold the Pullman stock and the Bethlehem Steel, the proceeds from which were sucked into the coffers of three expensive colleges. The house would probably go next year. As for the children? How could he hold onto them?

"The empty nest syndrome," Saul Radner said once, after a squash game. "You'll get over it. We did. It's worse if they come back, believe me."

Maybe. In any case, Cooper knew from experience what it was like for a man and a woman to move well together on a common enterprise. The sounds and rhythms of his old domestic dance with Liz still echoed through their empty house, through their present life. Maybe he wanted to bring back Jack and Kitty as a way of reconfirming that such a dance could still be done.

8

Nobody could really say exactly when it was that Jack started dancing with Kitty. Because he came into dancing school the middle of the second year, Mr. Van Dam was already concentrating on partner dancing, so they must have danced together a number of times without anybody noticing anything particular about them. After all, there were elaborate procedures for making sure that everyone danced with everyone else, and the taller or less compelling girls weren't left sitting endlessly on the sidelines. Jack never spoke about Kitty to the gang at Smither's, or if he did, he never mentioned her in any special way, or even if he did that, it was no more special than the way the other boys spoke about her. Similarly, none of Kitty's friends could recall any particular point when she might have begun to squeal or gush about the new Irish boy from the west side. Of course, Kitty didn't have that many friends, except maybe in Maine, where she went for the summer. Besides, she wouldn't really squeal or gush anyway. Not Kitty. She might roll her eyes, or sigh if something excited her, or more likely if she wished it excited her more. But she'd never gush. In any case, nobody had an inkling that anything special had gone on between them.

For Cooper, for everyone, the thing seemed to happen suddenly, that night when Kitty came in late. It was in the spring, late spring, after spring vacation, as a matter of fact, because Kitty had been to Bermuda with her parents. Into the ballroom she came, tan and gorgeous in a new white dress, after everybody else had already shaken hands and chosen partners and was trying to learn the rumba. It was one of those unusual evenings when everyone had paired up, and there were no extra girls sitting along the side. A couple of girls were dancing together, but still, everyone was paired.

Kitty stood in the doorway and looked around, and you could almost hear her say, "Hmmm." Everyone else began looking at her too, over their shoulders or over somebody else's shoulder as they tried to keep up the dance. Mr. Van Dam saw her, and then suddenly began tapping his stick rapidly on the floor. Mr. Cromeier stopped playing "The Lady in Red" or "Orchids in the Moonlight" or whatever it was, and also looked at her. Mrs. Foster and the several parents who were there that night turned their heads and looked at Kitty Price, standing alone, tan and lovely, in the doorway of the Grand Ballroom at the George Washington Hotel.

There was silence for what seemed like a long time. Then, "Good evening, Miss Price," Mr. Van Dam said.

"Good evening, Mr. Van Dam," said Kitty, with a tiny little bob and an almost imperceptible sigh, as if to say she knew she was supposed to curtsy, or do *something* stupid, but she really didn't want to, so she guessed she wouldn't.

Cooper Jones, who was standing close to Jack Daley, thought he heard Jack give a strange, deep groan.

"I believe you're late, Miss Price," said Mr. Van Dam.

"I know. I'm sorry," she said, staring him down. Cooper thought it was pretty classy that she didn't even bother to give an excuse. And he heard Jack groan again.

"We are learning the rumba," Mr. Van Dam said. "And I believe everyone has already found a partner."

"Then I'll just sit this one out," Kitty said, starting across the floor to the row of empty chairs where the girls always sat.

Because it was late in the year, Mr. Van Dam may have been more irritable and impatient than usual with Kitty's tardiness. Because it was spring, he may have taken an extra nip from his silver flask under the stairs by the cloakroom. Because it was the rumba, he may have been more discouraged than usual by the clumsy steps and inaccurate rhythms of the class. Or maybe he was simply enticed by Kitty's lovely tan shoulders and back, set off by the thin, white straps of her dress, as she walked slowly away from him. In any case, he suddenly called out, "Stop!"

Kitty stopped, in the middle of the floor, and turned, and looked at him rather quizzically, as if she were trying to determine whether that strange, hoarse bellow had actually come from him.

Mr. Van Dam took his time. He went and laid his stick

very neatly across three chairs. Then he walked slowly out to the center of the ballroom where Kitty stood waiting, watching him.

"You will dance with me," he said, bowing elegantly in front of her.

"You?" said Kitty, now definitely *not* curtsying.

"Me," said Mr. Van Dam. "We will dance together. Music, Mr. Cromeier, if you please." And he held out his arms to Kitty.

But by this time, Jack was noticeably panting and straining like a dog on a leash, and before the music could even begin, he yelled out, "Hold it! Wait a minute!" and left his partner, and loped out toward the center of the room. *"I'll* dance with her," he said, looking straight at Mr. Van Dam, fixing him with his keen direct gaze.

Mr. Van Dam showed admirable restraint. "I believe you already have a partner, young man," he said. "I believe you were already dancing with Miss Dilloway."

"She doesn't get the rhythm," said Jack. "She can't follow me at all."

There was a gasp of horror from several of the girls. A few of the boys laughed. Dootsie Dilloway, who was tall, thin, and notoriously shy anyway, turned bright red and covered her face with her hands. Several other girls left their partners and gathered cooingly around her. The parents sitting in the visitor's section murmured anxiously among themselves. Kitty said "Egad" under her breath. Things were breaking up.

Mr. Van Dam's mouth opened and closed. He looked like a great frog, his neck puffing over his starched white collar.

Jack looked around and quickly tried to make amends. "Tell you what," he said. "I got an idea. You dance with Dootsie. I think she needs special help. I'll dance with Kitty Price. O.K.?"

Everyone began to laugh at this point, except for poor Dootsie and Mr. Van Dam, who turned away grimly and strode across the floor to retrieve his stick. Rat-a-tat-tat. The machine gun sound echoed through the room, and people quieted down but quick.

"Very well," said Mr. Van Dam carefully. "We will all take our seats and watch Mr.—what's the name again, young man?"

"Jack. Jack Daley."

"We will take our seats and watch Mr. Daley teach Miss Price the rumba."

"Oh, Lord," said Kitty softly, rolling her eyes toward heaven.

Jack touched her arm.

"Sit down, please, everyone," said Mr. Van Dam. "Everyone be seated." So everyone retreated, the girls to their side, the boys to theirs, and sat down.

Jack and Kitty stood facing each other. Mr. Van Dam turned, crossed the floor slowly, and sat down himself, very carefully, legs apart, hands folded neatly on top of his stick which he kept upright in front of him.

"Now," he said, "the young gentleman will ask the young lady to dance."

Jack gave Kitty a beautiful bow. She looked at him for a moment, and then gave him back a lovely curtsy. It was a deep curtsy, it was a slow curtsy, it was still a slightly ironic

Kitty curtsy, but she looked great doing it, there in the center
of the ballroom, curtsying to Jack in front of Mr. Van Dam
and the entire class.

"Music, Mr. Cromeier, if you please," said Mr. Van Dam.
Mr. Cromeier, who had been enrapt in the situation himself,
snapped to attention, turned to his piano, drew his fingers
down the keyboard in a long, swooping scale, and then
surged into the melody. And Jack and Kitty danced.

That was the first time people saw how good they were
together. They had the whole floor to themselves and they
made the most of it. Kitty may never have danced the rumba
before, but Jack pulled her in close to him and held her tight,
and she managed to pick up his beat. Or rather, *almost* pick
up his beat. She was still, even in the rumba, just a little bit
late, just a hair, just a fraction of a fragment of a second, so
that there was a slight lag or gap between what he did and
what she did, as if he were giving her the lead and she were
deciding to follow. It was absolutely terrific. They took tiny
steps, or not steps even—they made tiny moves, but they
seemed to glide swiftly all over the dance floor in their wonderful, odd, syncopated gait.

Mr. Cromeier, who was watching them out of the corner of
his eye even as he played, must have become inspired by
seeing, for possibly the first time in his life, a really good
couple dance to his tired old arrangements. Soon his music
took on a special life and excitement. Just when you thought
he was going to end, he'd modulate into another key and do
another song, and then another, his fingers rippling over the
keyboard, his head bobbing, the man actually smiling for the
first time anyone could remember. And as he added his riffs
and runs and elaborations, so did Kitty and Jack add riffs of
their own, little spins and turns and breaks, with Kitty oc-

casionally rolling her eyes to the ceiling even as she did them, as if she were still saying, "Help. Eeek. Egad. What am I doing? Where am I going? What do I do *now*, for heaven's sake?" And when Mr. Cromeier finally came to the end of his medley, he gave it a complicated, elaborate finish, and Jack spun Kitty out to the side, as they do in the movies, so that they ended up with Jack holding her just by her fingertips, bending toward her as Kitty dropped into a deep, deep, deep theatrical bow.

Well, there it was. Everyone in the room stood up and burst into loud applause. The boys whistled and catcalled as if they were at a Friday night hockey game. The girls shrieked and squealed. From one visitor's section, several parents cupped their hands and called "Bravo!" and "Well Done!" Mr. Cromeier stood up by his piano, beaming and applauding.

Mr. Van Dam was impressed, too. You could tell. He didn't clap, but he stood up and looked around the room, taking in the cheering rather proudly, as if the cheers were really for himself. When the noise began to die down, he rapped his stick on the floor, and of course there was silence almost immediately, because everyone wanted to hear what he had to say.

"That was very good," he said to Jack and Kitty, walking out to meet them as they stood, panting and beaming, in the center of the floor. "Very good indeed." Everyone clapped and cheered again.

"I can see, young man," he continued, "that you've been paying attention. And you, Miss Price, must have been practicing on your own."

"No. I just followed him," said Kitty, with one of her weird, lopsided smiles.

"Well, you may take your seats, indeed you may sit

together, and watch the rest of us try to learn from your example," said Mr. Van Dam.

So Jack and Kitty made their way to the chairs, surrounded by congratulatory throngs, and finally, after they sat down, Mr. Van Dam got everyone to try the rumba again. Cooper thought, a number of people thought, even a few of the watching parents thought, that everyone danced a little better that night after seeing Kitty and Jack.

Who knows what Mr. Van Dam thought? There were only two or three more sessions before dancing school ended for the summer, and he conducted them pretty much as he conducted all the others. There were a few subtle changes, though. At the beginning of the evening, when the young gentlemen were to ask the young ladies to dance, Cooper and all the other boys instinctively understood that Jack had the right to choose Kitty. So there was no more dashing across the floor or sliding into position in front of her. Everyone walked quietly and picked some other girl. This was when Cooper started picking Liz, for example. There were still procedures whereby you had to change partners a good deal of the time, but Jack and Kitty ended up together more than most. And when they danced, other couples would automatically get out of their way and give them extra room.

Mr. Van Dam almost seemed to ignore them, but he did now call Jack "Mr. Daley," if he spoke to him at all. Kitty was half an hour late to the second to last session, but Mr. Van Dam took no notice of it, and when Jack politely took whomever he was dancing with back to her seat so that he could dance with Kitty, Mr. Van Dam took no notice of that, either.

After the final class, there was the Cotillion, where

everyone put on paper hats and ate ice cream and cake, served by a busboy named Kevin, who knew Jack from school and who winked at him as he came down the line with Kitty. Following the food, there was the dance contest. Mr. Cromeier brought in an accordionist and the saxophone players and even a man on the drums. They played a fox trot, a samba, and a Viennese waltz, and of course Jack and Kitty won all three, hands down. They were great: Jack stalwart, focused, and intense; Kitty casual, continually surprised, and always just a little bit late.

Mr. Van Dam, Mrs. Foster, and Mrs. Wilkinson were the judges, and Mr. Van Dam himself awarded the prizes: a silver tie clip for Jack, a silver bracelet for Kitty, with May, 1943, engraved on both, their initials to be put on later. When they received them, everybody yelled, "Encore! Encore!" Kitty looked at Jack as if to say, "Oh, God. What now?" and Jack looked at Mr. Cromeier, and before they knew it, they were doing a lively polka all around the room, to "Roll Out the Barrel," and they were great at that, too.

This time even Mr. Van Dam clapped, and then he held up his hand for silence and made a short speech. He said he had decided to retire. He had taught dancing in this city for over fifty years, he said, and enough was enough. Cooper noticed Mrs. Van Dam standing unobtrusively in the doorway, watching. It was the first time, to his knowledge, she had ever come upstairs.

Everyone was surprised by Mr. Van Dam's announcement. A few parents in back shouted, "No!" but he held up his hand, and they quieted down. His pupils were by now well enough trained so they didn't cheer. They applauded politely, and without being told, lined up to shake hands with him as they left. Jack and Kitty said good-bye to him, too, but he didn't say anything special to either of them.

Later that summer, several people saw him sitting out on the porch of his second story apartment on Ashland Avenue. He was wearing an undershirt, and drinking a beer, and reading the *Evening News*. There was a small notice in the same paper the following fall saying that he had died of a heart attack.

Some of the more mean-spirited parents said that he retired because he was a snob, and could not abide having to give a prize to an ambitious Irish boy with an unknown background. Cooper Jones didn't agree with that opinion at all. He felt sure that Mr. Van Dam was simply quitting while he was ahead. He couldn't do better than Jack and Kitty, and he knew it. And the following year, on the Sunday after Christmas, down at Trinity Church, when Cooper was sitting in the family pew and listening to the choir sing the Nunc Dimittis—"O Lord, now lettest Thou Thy servant depart in peace, according to Thy word"—he thought of Mr. Van Dam departing from the scene like the old priest in the temple who wanted to die once he had seen the real thing.

9

Dunlop, Potter, and Jones, Real Estate and Insurance, was the oldest real estate agency in Buffalo, and indeed one of the oldest continuing firms west of Albany. Established in the 1870s by Cooper's grandfather and old E. G. Potter, it was a thriving operation almost from the beginning. The Civil War was over, the Erie and Barge Canals seemed to be teeming with traffic to and from New York, the railroads had settled on Buffalo as a major terminus, and endless carloads of coal, grain, beef, and iron ore began arriving on their way east. Huge warehouses and grain elevators and then factories sprang up along the lake and stretched down the Niagara River to where the Falls were being harnessed for electrical power. Poised as it was at the eastern corner of Lake Erie, where the lake spills into the blue Niagara, Buffalo ("Beau-Fleuve") looked both east and west: east, toward the crowded markets of New York and Boston and Hartford and Philadelphia; west, over the vast waterways of the Great Lakes to where the infinite American and Canadian territories lay waiting to be explored, cultivated, and developed. What was Detroit? A trading post out there, somewhere. What was Chicago? A railroad station and a corral. Buffalo was "The Queen City of the Great Lakes," "The Gateway to the Future," "An Eastern Gal with a Westward Look."

Cooper's grandfather sensed the pulse and energy of the city even fifty miles south on his family's farm. He came to town, worked hard, improved his education, married a reasonably rich girl, and tied up with old E. G. Potter. They'd take a horse and buggy out along the river or the lake and buy tracts of land from farmers whose children were leaning on their hoes and looking restlessly toward town. Cooper's grandfather knew how to talk their language, and old E. G. knew how to borrow money, and before long, both gentlemen were possessors of impressive chunks of valuable property, which they sold at considerable profit to the steel companies and other industries who needed waterfront sites for cooling, sluicing, and flushing during the manufacturing process. Later, the two entrepreneurs brought Dave Dunlop into the firm because he owned half the buildings downtown, and wanted to own the other half, and before long the three dominated the real estate situation in Buffalo. Cooper's grandfather made quite a lot of money and spent relatively little of it. Cooper's father, who of course went into the business, made a little more, and spent a lot more than that. And so it went, yea, unto the third generation.

Cooper didn't like being called a realtor, or a broker, or an insurance man. Those labels seemed somewhat demeaning.

No, he was simply "in" real estate, and indeed was now a vice president of the company, the president being Jake Klinger, who had come in after the war. Cooper had worked there as a runner and office boy for several summers while he was still in college, and after he graduated and served in the Navy and got married, he didn't think twice about wanting to work there full time. He spent six weeks in Hartford taking a crash course for his insurance license and another month in New York acquiring one for real estate. Then home he came, to settle in, first at a desk in the outer office next to Mrs. Klinck, the bookkeeper, then at a larger desk in a cubicle of his own, and finally, after his father died, at his father's desk in the inner office, where his grandfather had sat, too.

The firm still had most of the ground floor on the southern side of a stolid old building which was of enough architectural merit to have been spared the wrecking ball during urban renewal. It was good space. It felt good to walk into. There was a lot of burnished old oaken furniture, and a thick forest-green rug, and old photographs and prints of the city in its heyday all around the walls. The office staff was fairly well paid and fairly happy. The younger members of the firm—most of whom were descendants by blood or marriage of Dunlop or Potter or Jones—had decent expectations, and the older members, like Cooper or his Uncle Paul or Jack Klinger, got along fine. There was a vaguely Victorian atmosphere about the place—Dickens without Scrooge—which was reinforced by lively and sentimental Christmas parties, strong echoes of family and continuity, and an amused tolerance of the idiosyncrasies of those who worked there. So what if old Uncle Paul fell asleep at his desk every afternoon? So what if young Howard Dunlop was hopelessly absent during the duck hunting season? So what if Miss Marek chewed gum? Business was still done, what business there still was. And there was still enough, after all. When you tallied things up, you realized that this fine old firm had put bread on the table and clothes on the backs of three generations of Dunlops and Potters and Joneses, as well as helping to educate them for the world beyond—or at least for a decent career at Dunlop, Potter, and Jones.

Cooper always enjoyed coming into the office, saying good morning first to Mrs. Rudd at the switchboard, then to whoever was looking up at him across the low partitions, then to his secretary Miss Kovak, and finally to his Uncle Paul if he were in that morning, and whose desk was right next to Cooper's now that Cooper had taken his father's place. On this particular morning, the morning that Liz had intervened at breakfast about the Snow Ball, the morning he had walked around his house and particularly missed his children, there was already a telephone message waiting for him on his desk: "Call Lucy Dunbar ASAP." So he did, immediately, knowing it was about the Snow Ball.

"You saw the little article in the paper," he said.

"Did I! I'm thrilled."

"It kind of makes the whole idea seem official, doesn't it?"

"I'm absolutely thrilled, Cooper. I've been on the telephone ever since I read it."

"Liz thinks it's a dumb idea," Cooper said.

"Oh well. You know Liz," Lucy said.

"I think I do. Yes." They both laughed.

"Actually," said Lucy, "we should get together and start planning."

"Sure we should."

"Maybe lunch or something."

"That would be good."

"How about today?" Lucy said. "I'm frantic to get going."

"Today? Let me check my book." He did. Lunch time was blank, as usual. "All right. Today. The Saturn Club again?"

"No, actually. I don't want everyone breathing down our necks. How about some place downtown?"

"Let's see . . . " There was the Mid-Day Club, where he normally ate, but that excluded women. "Um . . . "

"How about the Crescent Moon?" said Lucy.

"The Crescent *Moon?*"

"It's a little Turkish place on the corner of Seneca and Eagle. Nobody goes there. We can really knuckle down."

"O.K. The Crescent Moon. One o'clock," said Cooper and hung up.

Then he went to work. Or tried to.

Cooper's specialty was houses. He knew houses cold. His grandfather may have been good at acquiring land, and his father may have been good at renting space and managing buildings, but Cooper was good at dealing with where people lived. In recent years, the younger members of Cooper's firm were beginning to involve themselves with suburban developments and shopping centers and condominium complexes, but Cooper stayed with houses, particularly older houses, particularly in town.

So, like his forefathers, he was good at what he did. He liked doing it, which helps, and people liked having him do it, which helps more. "If you want to sell your house," they'd say, "call Cooper Jones." Or, "If you have to move to Buffalo, at least let Cooper Jones sell you a house." He certainly did know how to show houses. He knew the best time of day to approach them, the most attractive direction from which to drive up, and the most enticing place to park the car. He knew which door to enter by, which rooms to show first and last, and how to make the cellar seem trivial and unimportant. He knew how to steer someone gently by the cracks in the ceiling or the stains on the wallpaper into the renovated kitchen and the sunlit garden beyond.

It wasn't that he was dishonest. Far from it. The reason he did so well was that he was a dreamer about houses, and in a sense he dreamed aloud. As he guided a client through the various rooms, he would manage to convey, through his comforting spiel, compelling images of domesticity: tremendous parties in the living room, tremendous meals in the dining room, tremendous sex in the master bedroom. He could see around corners, too. He was a master at suggesting revisions and renovations. "You could do wonders with that attic," he'd say, for example, and suddenly you'd be seeing a light, spacious loft with skylights, and built-in bunks, and fold-away desks where rows of well-behaved children concentrated quietly on their homework. "I can almost see a pool in that yard," he'd say, and you'd imagine yourself floating at your ease in clean, sparkling, easily maintained water under an azure sky.

You almost might say that to Cooper a house was like a woman, and he danced with her the way Jack Daley danced with Kitty Price. He treated her with pride, courtesy, and a touch of reverence, and took great joy in displaying her to her best advantage. Houses seem to breathe a little easier when Cooper approached them and did his bows in front of them, and they seemed to settle proudly back on their foundations when he finally closed the door and walked away.

Which is not to say he wasn't a good negotiator. He inherited his grandfather's instinct for bargaining and his father's instinct for tact. He knew how to ease the buyer up and the seller down. He had a nose for what was the fair and equitable price, and saw that most negotiations landed on or near it. People trusted him on both sides of the fence, and nobody walked away from passing papers on a house that Cooper Jones had been involved in without feeling it had been a damn good deal.

And finally, he stirred the pot a little. When Cooper arrived at his office in the morning, he didn't simply settle down and fiddle with the listings and wait for the telephone to ring. He dialed it himself. He had a nose for who might be ready to sell and who might be ready to buy, and more times than not, he made it happen. Cooper was the one who persuaded old Mrs. Cooke to consider giving up her lovely little house on Linwood. He got the Stevensons, who now had two children in college and were talking about something smaller, to drive by it with an architect. And he knew that the Careys, with their new baby, would be ripe for the big Stevenson house. And he told old Mrs. Cooke that the Carey apartment in Mayfair Lane might be coming on the market. He got the whole thing going. He sold three domiciles in one day, and made three families at least temporarily happier—four, actually, if you count his own, since he took them all skiing out west on the commissions.

"Sometimes I think you're a manipulator," Liz said, though she didn't say it while they were skiing. "You run this vast game of musical chairs all over town."

"I don't accept the analogy," Cooper replied. "In musical chairs, somebody loses. With me, everyone wins."

Which wasn't quite true. Liz thought of the Gravelys.

When they couldn't keep up the mortgages, Cooper persuaded them to sell to the Horowitzes. And he sold the Horowitz house to the Paganos. And he sold the Pagano house—which was a two family double decker—to an extremely congenial black family named Moorhead, who now rent the lower half to a family of Boat People named Nang. But he obviously couldn't put the Gravelys out in the project on Jefferson where the Moorheads came from, so he gave them to Dodie Atwater in the suburbs and they never were heard of again.

So there were some losses in this vast dance for dwelling places which Cooper was constantly stirring up all over town. And some disappointments, as well. Sometimes people would find themselves sitting on a packing crate in the middle of the stark, white-painted living room of a house Cooper had just sold them and wondering why the hell they were there. The Folkersons got in just such a state, and had to go to a family therapist about it, and finally the only solution was for Cooper to sell them back their old house at a considerably higher price.

"You're always stirring things up," Liz said, after this particular incident. "Your mother says the same thing. When you were young, you'd wander from room to room causing trouble. And now you're doing it on a city-wide scale."

"I like to make things better," Cooper said. "I like to improve people's lots, no pun intended. I also like to pay our bills."

"Well all I know is you make everyone restless and uneasy. We all wander around eyeing each other's houses. I think you create envy and suspicion around here, Cooper, if you want to know."

Of course, that was Liz, intervening again.

In any case, Cooper sold houses, and the more he bickered with his wife, the better he got at it. The more difficult his domestic life became, the more his yearning for the ideal home would pervade his realtor's harangue: "Imagine a seated dinner of your twelve closest friends being served in this room. . . . Can't you see yourself in this den, your wife sewing on the couch, your children playing Chinese Checkers in the corner, a fire blazing, a dog at your feet, reading a book and listening to Bach while a storm rages outside that triple-glazed thermopane window. . . . Look at this bathroom, look at these fixtures. Can't you imagine your wife splashing around in that sunken tub, singing selections from *South Pacific* while you shave at this double sink and prepare for another happy day." So it went. He put himself whole-heartedly into every house he showed and invited his clients to join him, so usually he made the sale. He was a mainstay in that area in his firm.

For the past week or so, however, ever since the Snow Ball issue had come up, things had changed a little. Cooper seemed much vaguer in the office. He made fewer telephone calls, studied fewer listings, and spent much less time showing houses. He lost several sales too. His mind wasn't on his work, that was clear. Even old Uncle Paul noticed it and asked him if he were having trouble at home. Dodie Atwater, the aggressive young divorcée who focused on the suburbs, thought that it was simply male menopause. "I know whereof I speak," she said to Jack Klinger. Miss Kovak, Cooper's secretary, suspected he was having an affair, possibly with Lucy Dunbar, who kept making these telephone calls. "I used to wish he'd have an affair with me," she confided to Mrs. Klinck, the bookkeeper, at lunch, "but now I think he's too spaced out."

Of course, it was simply that Cooper had latched onto a different dream, that's all. No longer was he imagining ideal domestic scenes in tastefully refurbished old houses. Now his mind was mostly on the Grand Ballroom at the George Washington Hotel, and what ideally could happen there. And what ideally could happen was the Snow Ball, and Jack dancing with Kitty once again. He had moved people from space to space for quite a while. Now he wanted to mess around with time. Kitty and Jack, together again on the dance floor after thirty years. The thought began to obsess him.

And so when he showed up at the Crescent Moon to meet Lucy for lunch, he was eager to get going, to make plans, to put the Snow Ball on the market, so to speak. He brought along a large yellow pad and several sharpened pencils, and as they talked, he made notes and lists and even diagrams of the ballroom. They talked about music and decorations and liquor and food. They figured out costs and times and various deadlines. They discussed who would want to take tables and who might give dinner parties beforehand. And they worked very carefully on how and when to approach Jack and Kitty.

It was a good lunch. And a long lunch. Cooper and Lucy worked well together. They worked so well that Lucy didn't really pay much attention to their surroundings, to the sultry atmosphere and insinuating music which pervaded the Crescent Moon. She hardly even noticed her food. Cooper did. He noticed what he ate, and where he was, and he noticed Lucy. He noticed she was rather attractive, at least in that Levantine light, and she seemed increasingly so when she moved over to his side of the table so they could review his notes together. It was a pleasure to work so closely with a woman. He hadn't really had this feeling since he and Liz had systematically assembled the children's toys on Christmas Eves long, long ago. At the end of lunch, he said to Lucy that this seemed like a very congenial place to meet and work, and they should plan to meet there again in the near future. After they had made contact with Jack and Kitty, for example, and had something more to show.

Lucy agreed, and gave him another soft, damp kiss goodbye, very much like the one she gave him on his fiftieth birthday.

10

You'd think that after Jack and Kitty won the first prize at the dancing school Cotillion, they would have gone on dancing together on up through the Junior Assemblies and the Nine O'Clock Club. You'd think they would have danced their way through the next three or four years until they reached the Snow Ball. That's what you'd think, but actually that didn't happen. The fact was that for several years after they won, they didn't see much of each other at all. Kitty went away for the summer, of course, and then went off to boarding school in the fall, and seemed to come home for vacations only rarely. And Jack spent most of his time either studying or working in construction or playing sports for Nichols School.

Because he had gotten into Nichols now. He had transferred from Holy Angels the fall after the Cotillion. Cooper

Jones and a number of the other boys had urged him to do it, and several of their parents made telephone calls to Mr. Jenkins, the director of admissions, recommending he consider "that nice Irish boy who did so well at dancing school." Jack's parents, from all reports, were not terribly enthusiastic about his leaving a good Catholic school to hobnob with the Yankee types of the Delaware Avenue district, but Jack must have persuaded them it would be "good for his career." And the clincher was probably Kitty's father, who was there the night Jack and Kitty won the Cotillion. Apparently he was so impressed that he called up Bob Cutler, the headmaster of Nichols, the very next day and donated fifty thousand dollars to the scholarship fund. "I don't want to dictate who should be the recipient, Bob," he said, "but I do know that Daley boy is a winner."

So Jack came into Nichols for his Third Form (or ninth grade) year and did well almost immediately. He could only print, rather than write cursively, and his math was way behind, but his Latin was good, and he worked like a dog and made the Honors List by spring. As at dancing school, he'd be one of the first ones there in the morning, waiting outside the homeroom until Mr. Benbow, the janitor, unlocked the door. But while he waited, he never got into the yo-yo tournaments or mumplety-peg contests or eraser fights that took place before the bell rang. He always hunkered down at his desk and prepared for class. After sports in the afternoon, he'd come back to study hall even when he didn't have to. "If I go home," he told Cooper, "I'd just have to sit at the supper table and listen to my old man pick on my mother."

On the other hand, he wasn't just a grind. He was lively

and sharp and even fresh in the classroom. For example, in an oral report on Virgil, he said, "So Aeneas bade farewell to Dido, and thus began the Pubic Wars." He was also an excellent athlete and extremely popular with his peers. By his Fourth Form year, he was vice-president of his class, and then president for each of the two years after. He organized a club to support Dewey for President, captained the baseball team even in his Fifth Form year, and was voted the most valuable player in interschool basketball two years running. He worked every summer on highway construction and in the post office every Christmas. His father got him those jobs.

But if Jack danced into that world, Kitty danced out of it, at least for those four years. Off she went to Foxcroft, somewhere in Virginia, where she could keep a horse and where somebody else could take care of it. Her parents gave a sports party for her out at her grandmother's place in East Aurora the weekend before she left, and invited most of the dancing school crowd, including Jack. There was a lot of female shrieking and male croaking and pushing of people into the pool, but Kitty and Jack sat close together on the sidelines and watched. They didn't hold hands or fall into deep conversation or anything. They just sat there, as if they were beyond the horseplay by the pool, waiting for something more important to happen. Maybe they were waiting for the music to strike up from somewhere so they could dance. But no music did, so they just sat.

Later, over the hamburgers and hotdogs, Cooper asked her why she was going away to Foxcroft.

"Oh, well, Mummy went there," she said.

"No, I mean, why go to *boarding* school?" asked Cooper. "Why not stay here?"

"Well I don't want to spend the next four years arguing with Mummy," Kitty said. "Besides, maybe she's right. Maybe we're a little provincial in this neck of the woods."

"What do you mean, provincial?"

"Well, God. Look around. Everybody's starting to go steady."

It was true. People were beginning to pair up. Cooper himself was beginning to go out pretty consistently with Liz.

"You could go with Jack," Cooper said.

"That's another reason why I'd better go away," said Kitty enigmatically, and then they ran out of things to say.

So Kitty went to Foxcroft that fall. She was shipped down to Virginia with her horse and lasted six months before she was kicked out for smoking cigarettes. Fortunately, her parents knew someone on the board of Ethel Walker's in Connecticut, so they got her in there without skipping a beat. The horse no longer interested her particularly, so they gave it to a farmer.

At Ethel Walker's, from all reports, she got into trouble rather consistently from the moment she arrived. She was constantly late for classes and field hockey practice, she argued all the time about having to wear "that dopey uniform," and according to her report card, "demonstrated no class spirit whatsoever." When boys came over from Taft and Choate, she was always sneaking away from the housemother to neck with them in the woods, and on May Day, when they all were supposed to be up and singing school songs around the flagpole, Kitty had to be dragged out of bed. She would have flunked French, apparently, except that she had a strange affinity for irregular verbs. She passed just enough courses so that they had to graduate her, and she was voted "prettiest" and "messiest room" in her yearbook.

She came back to Buffalo very little on vacations. She'd be home for Christmas, but off skiing or down in the Bahamas before you hardly had time to call her up. In the spring she'd visit people all over the Eastern Seaboard, and in the summer she'd go right to Maine, so nobody saw very much of her for four years. It was as if she was purposely avoiding something.

Of course, if she had come home, she wouldn't have been able to dance very much. Maybe that was the thing. Maybe she knew that. Mr. Van Dam had retired, after all, and while Mrs. Foster found a nice woman from Rochester to come in and "try to keep things going," the boys and girls in Cooper's group seemed to have had enough of dancing school. The Junior Assemblies and the Nine O'Clock Club pretty much withered on the vine.

Oh, you could say there was dancing of a sort. Or rather anti-dancing. Everyone who was going steady—and that meant pretty much everyone—would meet on Saturday nights in the basement of someone's house and try to undermine everything Mr. Van Dam had taught them. They'd turn off all the lights and put on the slowest, slushiest records they could find, and then shuffle and sway around on the cement floor, draped all over each other, propping each other up, pressing their bodies against each other as much as they dared, feeling profound and morose and terribly sexy, all at the same time.

Most people called them make-out parties, and took turns giving them. Their parents called them petting parties and tried to discourage them. Whatever they were, Cooper Jones enjoyed them tremendously, and so did Liz. Neither one of them was much of a dancer, but they both were great at slouching around cellars. Their bodies fit very well together. Liz liked stroking the back of Cooper's damp neck, and Cooper liked burying his nose behind her ear. "It was just a neighborhood dance, that's all that it was," the music would sob, but oh, what it seemed to be to Cooper as he'd press his erection against Liz and then go neck with her on some ratty couch behind the ping-pong table.

Jack never went to these parties, possibly because he didn't go steady. All his friends at Nichols tried to fix him up, and several girls invited him to the more formal dances at the Buffalo Seminary, but he didn't seem to want to pair up. He claimed he had to study on Saturday nights, particularly since he normally had a basketball game on Fridays.

"Besides," he said, "if I got involved in stuff like that, I'd be spending all my spare time at confession." Everyone laughed noisily and let him alone.

But one night at a basketball game when Nichols was playing Jack's old alma mater, Holy Angels, Cooper noticed a dark, sexy girl with a lot of lipstick and a tight sweater yelling like crazy for Jack from the visitor's bleachers on the other side of the gym.

"Who's the babe?" he asked one of Jack's old buddies, whom he knew very slightly.

"Oh, that's Terri Tolentino, Jack's girl," the buddy said.

"Jack's *girl?*"

"Sure. They've been going together off and on since eighth grade."

"I thought he stayed in Saturday nights."

The buddy laughed. "He stays in, all right." The buddy had been drinking beer out in the parking lot.

Cooper mentioned it to Jack the following Monday. "Hey, Jack, what've you been hiding?"

"Repeat the question, please," said Jack.

"I'm talking about Miss Terri Tolentino."

"A friend," Jack said, with a wink. "An old acquaintance. A boyhood chum." And that's all he would say, no matter who teased him about it. He was very gentlemanly. He didn't kiss and tell.

Except one summer when Cooper met him looking a little rumpled and guilty at the popcorn stand at Shea's Great Lakes, where they were seeing *Destination: Tokyo.* Cooper had left Liz waiting in her seat, and he asked Jack whether he had brought Terri.

Jack nodded, and paid for his popcorn. Then he suddenly turned to Cooper and said passionately, "I gotta give it up."

"Popcorn?" said Cooper.

"No, you jerk." He nodded toward the back row, where now Cooper could see Terri, lit from the screen, combing her hair. "Her. It. It's no good. I feel like an animal!" And he was off before Cooper could reply.

Occasionally they'd hear, too, that Kitty had a new "beau" from some boarding school, or, one summer, a freshman from Princeton, but from all reports, nothing serious, nothing permanent. Liz had a cousin who went to Prout's Neck in the summer, who had been told by a boy from Bar Harbor that Kitty was frigid.

"How did he know?" asked Cooper.

"I don't know the details," Liz said, "but that's the story, anyway. That's why she plays the field so much. She has to keep moving so no one can pin her down."

"I'll bet Jack would pin her down," said Cooper.

"Maybe that's why she stays away," said Liz.

In any case, for four years there, after they had danced at the Cotillion, Jack and Kitty hardly saw anything of each other. Jack had his life at Nichols and his summer jobs which helped pay for it and Terri, apparently, on the side, and Kitty was away at school and away in the summer and away almost every other vacation. Possibly they wrote each other letters—there was a lot of letter writing in those days—but if they did, it probably wasn't a thrilling correspondence. Jack was a very stiff writer, as Mr. Waterman kept telling him in English class. His compositions were flat and boring and full of expressions like "Thus we can see." Kitty wrote occasional letters or postcards to her friends in Buffalo, and these were downright silly, peppered with odd little drawings and unnecessary exclamation marks, and not saying much of anything except "Help!" "Yipes!" and "Jiggers! The Cops! I gotta go . . ."

No, it was doubtful that Jack and Kitty were secretly cranking out volumes of romantic literature, like Heloise and Abelard, because of their enforced separation. And it was doubtful that they carried on passionate telephone conversations either, because nobody called long-distance in those days except when they needed money or their grandmother died. Dancing was what Jack and Kitty were good at. Dancing was what had brought them together. And dancing was what they were destined to do.

11

DUNLOP, POTTER, AND JONES
Real Estate and Insurance
Serving Buffalo for over 100 years.

March 30, 1983

The Honorable John X. Daley
Lieutenant Governor
The State House
Indianapolis,
Indiana
46200

Dear Jack:

Remember me? I hope this letter finds its way to your illustrious door. We're all very proud here, by the way, of your accomplishments.

As you may know, the city is in the process of rehabilitating the old George Washington Hotel, through a combination of public and private funds. Even the old ballroom (shades of dancing school!) is being repainted and fixed up. A number of us are beginning to make plans to celebrate its completion by reviving the Snow Ball the Friday after this coming Christmas.

Would you, as a distinguished and honored alumnus of that glorious event, consider making an appearance at that time? We'd all be delighted to see you again, of course, and I have to say that your name would lend a special luster to the general festivities.

My best regards to your wife and children.

> Sincerely,
> /s/ Cooper
> Cooper Jones
> Vice President

Cooper was careful not to mention Kitty, or dancing, or anything like that. He simply wanted to make the first cast. The more complicated processes of hooking and landing the trout would have to come later.

As agreed in the Crescent Moon, Lucy Dunbar wrote Kitty on her personal note paper:

LCD

March 30, 1983

Dear Kitty-

I got your address from your sister, who said you had married again and were very happy in Florida. I'm so glad, Kitty. You've had quite a time. (Well, so have we all!)

Kitty, they're in the process of fixing up the old George

Washington Hotel downtown, and Cooper Jones and I and a few others are trying to cook up a Snow Ball. Why not? The ballroom is being all fixed up and there's no point in having it just sit there. We thought we'd have it right after Christmas, just like the old days, with a good orchestra and evening clothes and everything.

Would you come, Kitty? Bring your husband. It would be so nice to have you with us again, particularly since you were one of the stellar attractions.

Do let me know when you can.

> Love,
> /s/ Lucy

Lucy, too, was careful not to mention Jack. For all she knew, that could scare her away at the start.

Jack's reply to Cooper was prompt and official:

STATE OF INDIANA
Office of the Lieutenant Governor

April 8, 1983

Dear Sir or Madam:

The Lieutenant Governor regrets that his schedule prevents acceptance of your kind invitation. He wishes me to express heartfelt thanks on his behalf.

> Sincerely yours,
> /s/ (Mrs.) Marie Windkoff
> Executive Assistant

There was a little handwritten note at the end:

The Lt. Gov. was out of town, but I read him your note over the telephone. He sends his personal regards.

Kitty's reply to Lucy, of course, came a little later, but actually rather promptly, for Kitty:

MRS. BALDWIN HALL
20 Pumpkin Cay
Ocean Reef,
Florida

April 11, 1983

Lucy m'love-

A voice from the past!—And proposing another Snow Ball! What a neat idea! My heart already is going thumpety-thump!

But seriously, I doubt if I can do it. I could never get Baldwin to come to Buffalo in midwinter, and I certainly couldn't leave him here at the time. His kids are coming down for Christmas vacation (gasp, sigh) and my own daughter is supposed to show up, too. It will be a madhouse, but I'm afraid my attendance is required in the kitchen and at the washing machine and occasionally on the tennis court!

Have a ball without me! (No pun intended.) Hugs to any and all you see!

Love,
/s/Kitt

Well, there it was. Two rather discouraging responses from two people preoccupied with other things. Cooper and Lucy met for lunch again at the Crescent Moon, and discussed the situation over moussaka and a small carafe of red wine. What they had planned to do was get a hint of a maybe from either Jack or Kitty and then use it to attract and lure the other.

"But now I don't know," said Lucy, looking from one letter

to the other. "They both seem to be slamming the door on us."

"Nonsense," said Cooper. "Our work is just cut out for us, that's all. May I have the letters, please?"

Lucy handed them across the table. Now Cooper had been an English major at Brown, so he was good at analyzing the implications of words. He took the letters one by one.

Jack's letter, or rather Jack's *secretary's* form letter, was simply a bureaucratic twitch, too automatic to be taken seriously. And the postscript indicated that Jack hadn't even seen Cooper's letter. Wait till he came home from whatever boring political excursion he happened to be on. Wait till he read the letter and thought about it. Jack was still available—Cooper was convinced of it—and they would damn well cast another line out to him later on.

And as for Kitty's response, her refusal was riddled with holes. The Snow Ball was a "neat idea." Her heart was already pounding. To "doubt" if you can do something is not to refuse. In fact, if you read carefully, her whole letter ached with a sense of yearning, a longing to come home, to face the music and dance.

"So what do we do?" asked Lucy.

"Call her," said Cooper, firmly.

"Call her?"

"Telephone her. Right now. Come on. We'll go back to my office and call Kitty."

So they did. Cooper introduced Lucy to Miss Kovak and guided her into the inner office, then sat her at Uncle Paul's desk, where she could be on the telephone too. Then he put in a person to person call to Mrs. Baldwin Hall at Ocean Reef, Florida.

A maid answered, but she went and got Kitty, and after a moment, he heard Kitty's voice: "Cooper Jones! Where are you? How are you? *Who* are you, these days?"

They exchanged the usual badinage. Cooper told her that Lucy was right there in his office, listening in. There was more delighted chatter, and then Cooper brought up the Snow Ball.

"Can't *do* it, darling," Kitty crooned. "I wrote Lucy. It sounds yummy, but impossible."

"It's not till next December, Kitty," said Cooper. "Can't you adjust your plans?"

"I can't adjust *Christmas*, sweetheart. God can, maybe, but I can't. And Christmas is the problem. I have to be here, not there."

"Let me at least put you down for a 'maybe,' Kitty."

"Stop it, Cooper."

"Just a 'maybe.' "

"Help me, Lucy!" said Kitty. "You're disgustingly quiet on the other end of that line."

"I want you to come, Kitty," said Lucy, on the other telephone.

"We all want you to come," said Cooper. "It's like a reunion. We want to get out a mailing saying who might show up. If your name is on the list, it will help bring other people."

There was a noticeable pause.

"What other people?"

"You know. People who are on the fence."

"Such as who?"

"*People*, Kitty. Whoever's around."

"Oh," she said, and Cooper thought he caught a faint echo

of disappointment. He looked over at Lucy, who shrugged.

"If you're on the list, Kitty," he went on, "people will know we're really rolling."

"Oh, phooey."

"They will, Kitty. After all, you were the star!"

Kitty laughed. "Some star. All I did was follow the lead." There was another pause, and then she said, "Tell you what. You can put me down for a weak 'maybe.' "

"Thanks, Kitty."

"That's marvelous, Kitty!" piped in Lucy.

"A very weak one, you two, and I mean it. A tiny little splash of a 'maybe' with plenty of bitters and ice."

Everyone laughed.

"I'm serious," Kitty went on. "I doubt very much if I can be there, but you can say 'maybe' if it will help."

Cooper and Lucy grinned and gave each other the thumbs-up sign there in his office, and after they had said good-bye to Kitty, they felt they had enough momentum to try to call Jack then and there.

They got through to his executive assistant, Mrs. Windkoff, without much trouble, but that seemed to be it.

"The Lieutenant Governor is in a meeting," she said.

"My name is Cooper Jones. I'm an old friend. Do you remember my letter?"

"I'd have to get it out of the files," she said.

"Well, would you tell him this: Kitty is thinking of coming."

"Who?"

"Better write it down, Mrs. Windkoff. Just write, 'Kitty is thinking of coming.' "

"Kitty?"

"That's it. Make sure he gets it."

After they hung up, Lucy said she ought to go. Cooper helped her on with her coat. They both were a little discouraged after only a half-baked nod from Kitty and what seemed like an impenetrable stone wall from Jack. Cooper walked Lucy to the door of the office and out onto the sidewalk, where they stood shivering in the spring wind, among the last patches of dirty snow, glumly discussing what to do next.

Then Miss Kovak came rushing out to tell him he had a long-distance telephone call from Indiana. He took it at the nearest desk, Lucy putting her head next to the receiver so that she could hear, too. It was Mrs. Windkoff, who said that she has just spoken to the Lieutenant Governor "who will come if he can, and hopes they'll keep him informed."

That was all. Cooper hung up and looked at Lucy, and suddenly they both were cheering and hugging like fans at a football game, much to the amazement of everyone else who worked at Dunlop, Potter, and Jones.

And later that week, Cooper had his last squash game of the season with Saul Radner and beat him easily, even on Saul's home ground.

"Hey, what's the story?" said Saul, while they were having their beers. "Suddenly you're turning into a real hotshot."

"I'm feeling pretty good these days," said Cooper. "I'm feeling twenty years younger."

"How come? What's going on?"

"Well, for one thing, we're really getting going on the Snow Ball."

Saul laughed. "Oh, come on, Cooper. I can't believe you're all turned on by some dance eight months down the pike."

"You wait, pal," said Cooper. "This won't be just some ordinary dance. This will be something really special. Remind me next fall, and I'll see if I can squeeze you in."

"Oh, we'll be all tied up with the Winterfest downstairs."

"That's what concerns me," said Cooper. "I'm scared we're going to steal your thunder."

Saul laughed and went to his locker to get dressed. "If I didn't know you better, Cooper, I'd say you had a girl."

"A girl?"

"You're acting like a guy who's got a girl somewhere."

"Oh yeah?" said Cooper, now getting dressed himself. "I should live so long." But even as he said that, he found himself thinking about his next lunch at the Crescent Moon with Lucy Dunbar.

12

In the center years of the twentieth century, Buffalo, New York, "Beau-Fleuve," "The Queen City of the Great Lakes," suddenly rolled over, sat up, rubbed its eyes, shook itself awake, and began frantically to dance. It was as if the seeds which Mr. Van Dam had planted so rigorously and meticulously for so many years, after a brief period of wartime dormancy, were now bursting forth in wild and exotic profusion. There were parties all over the place. Huge parties, elaborate parties, dances galore. They were called "coming-out parties," or if you wanted to sound slightly cheesy, "deb parties," but they really weren't that, at all. Oh, the newspapers would print pictures of grinning, white-gowned beauties, flanked by their parents in front of banks of flowers, and say that they were "debutantes" being "introduced" or "presented to society," but nobody was fooling anybody, unless it fooled the red-eyed, exhausted maids who served at these parties and then read about them in the early morning papers on the late buses home. No, "coming-out" was simply a lame and archaic way of describing what was going on. Nobody was coming out at all, unless she was coming out of the giggly confines of boarding school, or else coming out of the dank cellars where she had been festering like a mushroom for two or three years, swaying and stumbling, damp-haired and sticky-cheeked, pressed against the tentative erection of some pimply swain who had been her "steady."

Anyway, now there were parties. Luncheons, and teas, and tea dances, and dinner dances, and balls, balls, balls. They began in June, bloomed briefly in September, and then burst into full flower over Christmas vacation. Between your last fall term exam at college and New Year's day, you could go to a dance every night if you wanted to, and most people did, since there was nothing else to do. Mrs. Foster had her hands full scheduling the damn things, handing out lists, seeing that things happened, one after the other, without conflict or clash.

Indeed, the city became briefly famous for its parties. It earned a reputation which rippled up and down the East Coast. People came from all over to participate. Nieces, cousins, roommates from school would arrive trembling with anticipation at the airport or the railroad station, to be rushed headlong into the routine.

There was something strange about it, something almost desperate. Who started it? Why was it happening? What did it mean? There were all sorts of explanations for those who bothered to think about it. People were letting off steam after

114

the war. People who had made money in munitions were assuaging their guilt by sharing the wealth. The atomic bomb, the Russians, the Korean War already brooding on the horizon all contributed to the hectic, almost apocalyptic air.

Everyone got in on the act. Grandmothers and maiden aunts and godmothers got up from their chaises longues and gave dinner parties before the dances. Out came the old silver and the old crystal and the old china and the old servants, who staggered around the burnished tables, offering teetering platters of beef sirloin and fresh asparagus to troops of drunken adolescents on their way from one frantic festivity to another.

These dinners, actually, were crucial. The whole system depended on these dinners. They were where you got "paired up." Once a boy had "accepted with pleasure the kind invitation," a little card would arrive in the mail from the hostess saying, "Please escort Mary Jane Lewis," and that meant for the evening, Mary Jane was his. He had to pick her up, take her to the dinner, and *talk* to her during cocktails. He wouldn't be seated next to her at dinner—that would have been too much—but he had to drive her to the dance, "get her started" on the dance floor, dance with her at least one other time, and ultimately take her home.

He also had other obligations, of which he would be carefully reminded by his mother as she helped him with his collar studs and tightened his black tie. He had to dance (a) with the girl who gave the dance, (b) with the girl whose grandmother gave the dinner party, (c) with the girls who sat on either side of him at the table, and (d) with his sister, his cousin, and that poor soul with the unfortunate nose who was visiting the Robinsons. And if he didn't do any or all of these things, he would be personally throttled the next day.

The theory was, apparently, that if everyone followed these rules, if everyone lived up to these obligations, the party would end up a huge success. The more people danced, the more they changed partners, the more there was a continuous and ever changing swirl of activity, the better it was supposed to be. It was a little like a pyramid club. It required a serious commitment on the part of everyone involved, up and down the line. And so if someone broke the chain—didn't cut in on his hostess or ditched his dinner date—there could be a disaster. Someone might be "stuck" with someone else for at least five minutes on the dance floor. Someone might be found weeping in the ladies room. Or some boy—if he didn't keep dancing—might end up drunk. Oh, yes, there was a practical side to it. Dancing was exercise, after all, and you could drink a lot if you danced a lot. But if you stopped dancing and hung around the stag line with a glass in your hand, then you might end up barfing on the stairs or dead on the highway. It was better to dance, to keep moving.

So there were parties, and parties on top of parties, and for three or four years there, until the Korean War sucked him up and sent him packing, Cooper Jones spent most of his vacations from college going from one to the other. There were parties in houses, parties in clubs, parties in art galleries, parties in hotels. There were parties in Pittsburgh and Boston and Baltimore and Philadelphia. There was an intricate network of reciprocity up and down the Eastern Seaboard and reaching far into the west, through Buffalo to Detroit and Chicago and Minneapolis and St. Louis.

Confronted with this plethora of parties, Cooper became

very choosy indeed. He went to them all, but he got so he knew what was what. He became an expert, a connoisseur of parties. He knew the difference between a local combo and an imported orchestra from New York. He noticed who stinted on the flowers and who served the second-rate scotch. If they closed the bar before two, he complained bitterly, and if they refused to pay the band for an extra hour, he became seriously indignant. He appreciated it very much when they flew in the Whiffenpoofs to sing during intermission, and he offered special thanks when they served omelettes and sausages and coffee just before dawn.

Oh, he got very good about parties. He could sense when the rhythm was ripe for some serious cutting in, and when it made sense to lie low in the stag line. He knew how to shout funny comments into the ear of his partner as they were pumping around the room, and how to whisper sweet come-ons during the brief pauses when the musicians shifted to another set. He could tell by the way a girl danced—where she put her left arm, where she put her crotch—whether she was willing to make out, and how far she was willing to go. He knew the darkest parts of the country club lawns, and the softest couches in the remotest rooms. And when, at three or four in the morning, he finally drove home, or back to wherever he happened to be staying, half drunk, shivering in his perspiration, smelling of liquor and tobacco, speckled with lipstick, it all began to melt away, and by noon the next day, when he finally came down for breakfast, he had to rack his brain to remember where he had been, whom he had danced with, and whether or not he had had a good time.

"What jerks we were!" Cooper said to his children, years later, when they asked him about those days. "What absolute jerks! Skulking drunkenly around the bar, trotting aimlessly around the dance floor, ordering waiters and maids around as if we were gods—rude, careless, hopelessly unaware, poisoning our bodies, dissipating our souls, endangering half the town when we finally drove home. Good God! How could we have done it? How could we have been so dumb? There we were, in the prime of our lives, lost in these outrageous rituals of consumption and display, turning the magic and mystery of romance and courtship into a noisy, hectic exercise in perpetual motion."

"Oh, it wasn't quite that bad," said Liz.

"It was bad. It was terrible. I'll tell you what it was: it was the final, phosphorescent glow of a decaying culture, that's what it was. It was the last, spasmodic twitch of the corpse. And then we all took off our tuxedos, and put on our uniforms, and trotted off to fight yet another war on behalf of democracy and freedom and the pursuit of happiness, which to us consisted simply of this!"

Yet what about Jack and Kitty? What about them? Because they were there, too, all through it, starting in June. Kitty had graduated (just barely) from Ethel Walker's, and Jack (with honors) from Nichols, and of course they were both very much on the list. It was inevitable that they'd dance again.

Actually, it was Kitty's own party which really kicked off the season. There had been a few sporadic events in early June—a tea dance, a dinner dance—but they were just a warm-up for Kitty's coming-out party which was set for the middle of the month. She gave it at her grandmother's house out in East Aurora, which had been designed by Stanford

White. They had three bars, if you counted the one for older people set up in the library, and two orchestras. Harry Marchard brought in his first string from Boston, and they played on a special dance floor laid out on the terrace, overlooking the old polo fields. The local band was set up out by the pool, where there were rows of bathing suits and terry cloth bathrobes for people to put on in case anyone happened to be pushed in or wanted to be. Both the Nassoons from Princeton and the Night Owls from Vassar sang during intermission, and there was a charcoal grill going all through the night presided over by a special chef who came up from Hamburger Heaven in New York. Flowers were everywhere, most of them coming from Kitty's grandmother's gardens, except for a few exotic plants which had been flown in from Hawaii the night before.

Cooper arrived at about eleven, after a dinner party where Binkie Byers had taken all the tops of the asparagus when it was passed and had to be reprimanded by his hostess. Cooper was escorting Liz again, since Mrs. Foster was beginning to pair them up pretty regularly. Kitty stood between her parents in the main living room, shaking hands with a line of guests. She wore a white strapless evening dress which, Liz whispered, had been designed and made by Dior in Paris. She held a huge bunch of white flowers which made her arms look even tanner, and her hair had a few blonde streaks in it which must have come from lying on the roof of the dorm at Ethel Walker's and soaking up the spring sun. As she shook hands with Liz, she took an exaggerated tug at her bosom and announced that "this damn dress is being help up by nothing but faith." When Cooper got to her, she pulled him closer and whispered in his ear, "Dance with my roommate from Shaker Heights, and I'll be your slave for life."

And of course Jack was there too. Nobody had seen him at any of the earlier parties because he had already found a summer job on the new thruway, and had to be up at six most mornings, and so didn't have time to live it up. But now he was here at Kitty's, standing by the bar, talking with the bartender whom he knew from the old days at Holy Angels. He was already tan from working on the roads, and he was wearing what looked like a new tuxedo.

"Hey, you look pretty natty, Jack," said Cooper, going over for a quick drink while Liz got ready in the ladies room.

"It's tailor-made," Jack said. "It cost me four hundred and some bucks."

"Jesus Christ. How come?"

"I believe a man should try to look as good as he can," he said.

And he did. His shoes were immaculately shined, his pocket handkerchief emerged neatly by his lapel, and he had a stiff shirt and a starched collar and a cummerbund at a time when everyone else was easing into soft shirts and trying to look offhand and casual.

"Look at you, Cooper," he went on. "You're a slob. Your shoes need a shine and your pants don't even fit."

"It's my father's old tux," said Cooper.

"Yeah, well get your own," said Jack. "If you look good, you'll feel good. And if you feel good, you'll be a better dancer."

Once again, there was the wide grin, and the direct, no-nonsense gaze, which seemed to say you are the only person in the world I am interested in at the moment, and you are worthy of my complete and total attention.

They chatted for a while. Cooper talked about going to Brown in the fall and how he might try out for the soccer team. Jack had gotten an exceptional scholarship at Harvard because he had done so well at Nichols and because a number of distinguished Buffalo graduates, including Kitty's father, had written recommendations on his behalf.

"I decided on Harvard rather than Yale," Jack said. "Yale is involved with money and Wall Street. Harvard is concerned with government and power. I'll probably go right on to the Law School after I graduate. I see myself as a possible leader and shaper in a nation very much on the move." Suddenly he laughed, which made it all seem much less solemn and self-important. Then someone else came up to say hello to him, and Liz came to get Cooper to dance.

Jack didn't dance much, at least at first. He didn't have many duty dances because he hadn't gone to any of the dinners beforehand. He danced with Kitty a couple of times, and everyone looked to see whether they still had the touch, but it was hard to tell since the floor was crowded and someone else cut in almost immediately. He danced very politely with Kitty's mother, and Liz, and a couple of other girls, but that was about it. Most of the time he spent hanging around the bar, joking with his old buddy the bartender, holding court with whoever came up.

But then there was the dance contest. It was unusual to have such a thing at a coming-out party, but apparently Kitty wanted to have one, so her father announced it after the Night Owls had finished singing "Mood Indigo." There were groans and cheers as people struggled to their feet and sought out partners. Cooper and Liz were sitting with Jack

121

on the floor during the singing, but by the time they got up, he was already halfway across the room to where Kitty stood. He reached her, gave a wonderful, deep, Van Dam bow, and she gave her standard little sardonic curtsy, and then the music began.

Well, the dance contest was no contest at all. Before the orchestra had even finished the first medley from *Kiss Me, Kate*, the other couples had drawn back to form the same old space around Jack and Kitty. There they were, dancing again, better than ever, turning, gliding, dipping, Jack stalwartly leading, alert, eagle-eyed, constantly glancing ahead, charting out new territory into which he would guide her next, Kitty sleepy-eyed, slightly bemused, deliciously and dangerously late on most of her moves, occasionally taking her hand from his shoulder to give futile little hoists to her strapless dress, as if to say, "Ooops. Tsk. Tsk. Oh, well. Let the chips fall where they may."

They were really quite something. Harry Marchard and his orchestra, who were a little worse for wear at the beginning of the evening, having played till three A.M. in Chestnut Hill the night before and being due at nine the next night at a party in Grosse Point, seemed to gather steam as they saw this young couple dance their way out of the crowd. The music took on an additional bounce. Before long, there was a wonderful kind of exchange between the orchestra and the two young dancers, a kind of challenge, a kind of contest within the contest. "You play it—we'll dance it," Jack and Kitty seemed to be saying, until finally, as the beat went faster and faster, they broke into this long, fantastic, almost frenzied spin which looked as if it could have gone on forever if people on the sidelines hadn't started clapping and whistling and cheering so loudly that the music was drowned out and they had to stop.

And Cooper remembered thinking—thinking even then—that Jack and Kitty made it all make sense. They redeemed it all. The agonies of dancing school, these frantic, extravagant parties, and all the other silly rituals by which men and women tried to reach each other in that strange lost age—all, all seemed meet and right and wonderful when Jack Daley danced with Kitty Price. To see them move together with such twinkling charm, such easy grace, such subtle syncopation—this bright-eyed Irish boy, who took our world more seriously than it took itself, leading around this lovely, lazy girl who didn't take it seriously enough—surely something terribly profound was going on here. Cooper sensed it, and so did Liz, who reached for his hand and squeezed it while they were watching. Everyone sensed it as they all spilled out on the dance floor to crowd around Jack and Kitty when their dance was done. And when the music started up again, everyone danced with renewed energy and conviction and had a perfectly marvelous time.

13

In late September, when people had come back from the summer and were beginning to settle down, there was a big article in the Sunday edition of the Buffalo *News* about what was going to happen "over the holidays" at the reopening of the George Washington Hotel. Saul Radner and the Downtown Rehabilitation Committee spelled out in even more detail the various and disparate activities which would occur on the ground floor in the main lobby. Admission would be free, of course, and people of all ages would be able to wander among the booths and displays from six P.M. until midnight.

Upstairs, however, in the old ballroom, there would be what the paper called "the Snow Ball option." This would be "an attempt to revive the traditional post-Christmas society dance." It would require prepaid admission of one hundred dollars per couple to cover the costs of an orchestra and decorations, though there would be a cash bar. People were invited to get together and purchase tables of six to eight couples. Dress was optional, but black tie was recommended as being in keeping with the room and the occasion. Mr. Cooper Jones and Mrs. Lucy Dunbar, who were co-chairpersons of the event, were quoted as saying that they had invited some of the city's loveliest former debutantes to "grace the occasion," along with several native-born celebrities and public figures. (That was about as specific as Cooper and Lucy felt they could get without firmer commitments from Jack and Kitty.)

Nonetheless, a lot of people got the hint. Enough people were still around who had seen Jack and Kitty dance, and who had told their own children about it, so that there was already a tremor or two of excitement. Cooper's and Lucy's telephones rang more than once with inquiries about tickets and tables. Several women made plans to go down to New York in order to have something to wear. Poor old Mabel Callahan, who still served at dinner parties occasionally, despite her diabetes and her wooden leg, was already signed up to serve at the Frakes.

Cooper and Lucy felt slightly under the gun. They knew that for the party to be a success, they had to deliver Jack and Kitty—not just deliver them, but get them to dance.

"They might just stand around," said Cooper. "Shaking hands or something."

"Nonsense," said Lucy. "Put those two in that ballroom, give them a peppy orchestra, and off they'll go. No question. 'Fish gotta swim, birds gotta fly.' "

Cooper hoped she was right. Now that things were gaining

momentum, he was beginning to realize how bad the Snow Ball would be if Jack and Kitty weren't there. "It could turn into the *Masque of the Red Death*," he told Lucy. It would be a ghastly, ghostly parody of the old days which, without Jack and Kitty, were already ghastly enough: the evening clothes which people were beginning to get out of their cedar closets would look like ratty costumes from some forgotten, amateur play; the old show tunes, in their battered Lester Lanin arrangements, would sound tinkly and trivial. The whole evening would turn to dust unless it came together around Jack and Kitty. Oh, they didn't have to do a whole number. Just a few steps would do. All they needed *was* a flicker, a glimmer, a hint of what it could be like, what it once was like, when a man and a woman moved gracefully together around a lovely old room.

Cooper now also had a more personal stake in getting Jack and Kitty to dance. Since spring he had been carrying on a rather desultory affair with Lucy Dunbar. They had put their heads together in planning the Snow Ball, and then their bodies had seemed to want to follow suit. "It's called snow balling," said Cooper, after a furtive get-together, but Lucy didn't think that was funny.

It had begun almost naturally, after one of their exotic lunches at the Crescent Moon. They had shared a piece of baklava and a second cup of decaffeinated Turkish coffee, and were both reaching for the bill. "My turn," said Lucy, as she put her Visa gently on top of Cooper's American Express, as if she were trumping his ace. Their hands touched, their eyes met, and before they knew it, they were driving past the abandoned factories of Lackawanna toward the old Lakeshore Motel, where Randy Dann had once holed up with Melissa Fisk, and where her father had had to get the police to break down the door. "Why is it called Lackawanna?" he once asked his father. "It's an old Indian name," his father said. "It means lacka this, wanna that."

The motel was now sleazy and forlorn, but they bought a bottle of vodka at a nearby liquor store and some Mr. and Mrs. "T" Bloody Mary Mix, and toasted each other spunkily as they sat on the edge of the bed. Then they took off their clothes and popped in. It was no great shakes, they both agreed afterwards, but they were good sports about it all the same.

"After all, it's not the most conducive room in the world," Lucy said as she writhed back into her pantyhose.

"What?" called Cooper, who was in the shower, banging against the clammy tin walls.

"Skip it," she said, and they did. But still, possibly because things had been so unsatisfactory, they went there a couple of times again. And in June, when Liz had to go to Minneapolis for an interventionists' conference, Cooper and Lucy managed to spend the entire night together.

It was an easy relationship, in some ways. Lucy's children were away most of the summer visiting their father, so she and Cooper had the run of the house. Liz was particularly preoccupied by a reorganization of the staff at the hospital and was trying to intervene in *that*, so she really didn't keep tabs on what Cooper was up to. If Cooper and Lucy were occasionally seen together by their friends—if someone noticed his car parked in front of her house, for example—most people assumed that they were working together on the Snow Ball.

Which they were, really. It was very much on their minds,

most of the time. Their relationship was more of a courtship than a real affair. It was difficult even to feel guilty about it. They weren't terribly good with each other in bed, and they weren't terribly passionate about being with each other all the time, but they both felt that they might be once they had put Jack and Kitty back together. There was something vaguely anticipatory about the whole thing. They saw themselves as a kind of tentative trial run for Jack and Kitty, an introductory melody, a subplot, Gratiano and Nerissa setting things up for Portia and Bassanio. It was as if, by undergoing this little dalliance on earth, they could bring about a huge response in heaven.

And they each had unspoken expectations which they hoped would burst into bloom, like a Christmas cactus, at the Snow Ball. Lucy, for example, secretly hoped that at least *then* Cooper would realize how much more he had in common with her than with the sociological Liz, and so would negotiate a reasonably uncomplicated divorce and grow old with her in some convenient condominium. Cooper, on the other hand, had slightly less specific winter dreams. What he wanted, really, was just a good screw, a good fight, something. Extramarital affairs were supposed to be a lot more fun than this, and he hoped that Jack and Kitty would at least help bring things to a boil.

Meanwhile, they worked on, occasionally, at various times, slowly rolling the Snow Ball up the hill. By the end of September, they thought it was time to drop Jack and Kitty another note. "Just a reminder," they wrote, "of the Snow Ball on December 28. More later." They sent the same note to both Jack and Kitty, and they signed it "Cooper and Lucy." There was no immediate response from either Indiana or Florida, and they spent a lot of time wondering whether such silence was a good or bad thing.

And then, in mid-October, came some very pleasant news indeed. Ruth Spitzmiller, who had been to New York to see *Cats* and the Manet show at the Metropolitan, had run into Kitty, looking perfectly lovely, and shopping for a dress at Saks.

"What should I wear?" Kitty had asked. "I'm so out of touch these days I have no idea what people will be wearing."

"Wearing for what?" Ruth apparently asked, with her usual vagueness.

"The Snow Ball, of course."

Ruth seized the moment. "You mean you're definitely coming?"

"Natch," said Kitty. "Baldwin won't come of course. He hates things like that. But I'm thinking of flying up and flying right back. If I can find something to *wear*."

Ruth supposedly got very sly at this point. "It all depends on whether you plan to dance."

"I might," Kitty said.

"You might?"

"If anyone asks," and then she resumed pawing through things on the rack.

"I don't know whether she found a dress or not," Ruth told Lucy as soon as she got back to Buffalo, "but that's what she said, for what it's worth."

Lucy thought it was worth a great deal and telephoned Cooper at the office about it. They had lunch at the Crescent Moon to discuss it and got quite excited about it and actually had a rather good time in bed that same afternoon.

Later the same day, Cooper sent off a note marked "Personal" to the Lieutenant Governor's office in Indianapolis saying simply, "Dear Jack. It looks as if Kitty's definitely coming. Best regards, Cooper."

And less than a week after that, Cooper received a long-distance telephone call.

"Mr. Cooper Jones?" The operator's voice.

"Yes?"

"One moment, please."

Then a new voice: "Mr. Jones?"

"Yes?"

"This is Mrs. Windkoff, the Lieutenant Governor's assistant."

"Yes?"

"Hold on, please."

And then finally Jack's voice. "Cooper?"

"Hey, Jack!"

"How are ya, old friend?" Jack's voice sounded very much the same. Light, bright, slightly sharp. It was an Irish tenor, that's what it was. Cooper almost expected him to burst into song: "How Are Things in Glocca Mora?"

They went through the usual preliminaries for what seemed like an unusually long time. Wives, children, inquiries about careers, all that, and then Jack smoothly shifted gears.

"About this party, Cooper . . . "

"The Snow Ball."

"Right. The Snow Ball. Are things definite then?"

"Sure, Jack. The whole thing's planned."

"No, I mean . . ." There was a pause. Then Cooper heard him say, "Mrs. Windkoff, would you mind taking these

131

papers across the hall?" And another pause. And then he spoke more softly. "Is she coming, Cooper?"

"I think so, Jack."

"Definitely?"

"I think so."

Pause.

"Does she want to dance?"

"I don't know."

"Did you ask her, Cooper?"

"Do you want me to?"

Pause.

"I haven't danced in thirty years, Cooper."

"Come off it, Jack."

"I swear. Not in thirty years."

"Who has?"

"Has she?"

"I don't know, Jack. I doubt it."

"I wouldn't know where to begin, Cooper."

"It'll come back, Jack. It's like riding a bicycle."

He laughed. "Says who, Cooper?"

Another pause.

"I suppose we should dance," Jack said.

"I think so, too," said Cooper.

"Just a short spin, maybe."

"That's it."

"Just a quick turn or two around the floor."

"That's the way I saw it, Jack."

Cooper heard a buzzer in the background and some assistant saying something to Jack and Jack saying, "All right, hold it, I'll be right there."

"I've got a meeting, Cooper," he said into the telephone. "I've got to go."

"But hey, Jack, can we announce you'll be here? Can we tell the papers?"

Another pause.

"Yep. O.K. You can say I'll be there. If you're sure she . . ."

"She'll be there too, Jack. I promise," said Cooper, and they both hung up.

Then Cooper called Kitty immediately in Florida. Her husband answered, Baldwin Hall.

"Who is this, please?" he said.

"It's Cooper Jones. I'm an old friend from Buffalo."

"Oh, Christ." He called off: "Kitty!" Then back into the phone: "I think she's taking a nap."

Kitty picked up what must have been an extension. "I am not taking a nap. Now get off the telephone, Baldwin."

"Why don't you leave her alone?" said Baldwin and got off the line.

"Hi, Kitty. It's me. Cooper Jones again."

"You see what a grouch I married, Cooper? I married the world's worst grump."

Cooper told her about his conversation with Jack, how they'd probably be asked to dance a few steps, how he wanted to make a public announcement.

Kitty sounded very calm and quiet about it. "Well, I bought a dress, anyway. I might as well wear it. And I'm holding you personally responsible if Baldwin beats me black and blue when I get back. But as General Custer said before the Battle of the Little Big Horn, 'I'll be there.' "

And that afternoon Cooper and Lucy checked in at Lake-shore Motel and had one hell of a good time.

So it was announced in the Buffalo *News* that Jack Daley, son of Mrs. Edward Daley of Porter Avenue and now Lieutenant Governor of the state of Indiana; and Kitty Hall, formerly Kitty Price of Delaware Avenue, would be special guests at the revival of the Snow Ball on December 28. Suddenly things began to roll. Somebody on the newspaper did a little research and published a subsequent feature article on the old Snow Ball, when Kitty had been elected Queen, and she and Jack had won the Gertrude Palmer Cup. There were pictures from the old days and interviews with people who had seen them dance. Lucy Dunbar was quoted as saying that Jack and Kitty were "poetry in motion." Bucky King, who still shot under eighty out at the Country Club, said they were probably two of the greatest athletes to have come out of Erie County. And Fred McKinley, who had grown into something of an intellectual, said that certain things caused the hair on the back of his neck to stand up: "A 1941 Lincoln Continental convertible. A quadratic equation. And Jack and Kitty dancing." The Snow Ball became the hottest ticket in town.

And Cooper Jones became hot stuff himself. His squash, for example, was terrific. Now that it was fall, he had resumed his weekly games with Saul Radner, and he was winning every time, no matter on whose court they played. He was jaunty, aggressive, and adept. And once, after a particular rout, while they were having their beer, Saul pulled his leather chair a little closer and said, "Cooper, I wonder if you could do me a small favor?"

"Glad to," said Cooper, magnanimous in victory. "What can I do for you, Saul?"

"I wonder if you could get me into your Snow Ball."

"Hey, what about your Winterfest?" said Cooper.

"Oh, well, we'll be doing that too, of course. But later in the evening, a group of us want to come upstairs and see what's going on."

"Sure, Saul. I'll get you in. You and Judy?"

"Well actually the whole Winterfest Committee, with spouses, wants to come up. We'll pay, of course."

Cooper grinned and patted him on the knee. "I'll get you in, Saul."

"Thanks, Cooper." They got up to get dressed. "Oh, and do me a favor, Cooper. Don't publicize it. It wouldn't look good, if you know what I mean."

Cooper knew what he meant.

Cooper's affair with Lucy was now going strong, too. The closer they got to the Snow Ball, the more intense their relationship became. They saw each other more and more, and took more and more risks to be together. Susie Frake saw them coming out of the Statler, linked arm in arm, at three-thirty in the afternoon. "I suppose they were working on the Snow Ball," she told her husband later. "But then again, I'm not so sure."

And Liz got a strange anonymous note in the mail, written in a neat, boarding school hand: "Interventionist, intervene thyself!"

"What do you suppose this means?" she said to Cooper when he got home.

"Some crank," said Cooper, looking it over. "One of those

135

kooks from your job. Look, even the grammar's wrong. It should be 'intervene *in* thyself' or 'intervene *on* thyself.' " He went to the dictionary to look it up. Oh, he was very cocky.

And to top it off, at the end of November there was an article in *Time* magazine which said that the incumbent governor of Indiana had decided not to seek another term, and that the present lieutenant governor—"bright, up-and-coming Jack Daley"—would probably seek the Democratic nomination in March and run the following fall. So, my God! They would be having a future governor of a great state dancing right there, at their Snow Ball!

But then, suddenly, all smiles stopped. The telephone rang just as Cooper was getting ready to go up to bed. It took a minute or two before he realized he was talking to Baldwin Hall.

"She's just gone into the hospital in Miami," Baldwin said. "For a minor operation."

"Oh, no," said Cooper.

"She'll be all right. But she'll have to recuperate down here in the sun. She won't be able to come north for that goddam dance."

"I'm terribly sorry," said Cooper, and he meant it wholeheartedly. "Give her my best love."

"I will. I'd be glad to," said Baldwin gruffly, and hung up.

The next day Cooper sent flowers to Kitty in the hospital and put in a call to Jack, who was unreachable, doing some preliminary speechmaking in the southern part of the state. Cooper left a message with Mrs. Windkoff for Jack to call when he could. He thought it was only fair to let Jack off the hook, now that Kitty had cancelled. Mrs. Windkoff said she'd pass on the message, but Cooper could tell she didn't think the issue was terribly important. In any event, Jack didn't call.

That same week, Cooper lost three–love to Saul on his home turf, and had a series of messy and unpleasant arguments with Lucy. They both agreed that their relationship was probably a serious mistake. They had been living on dreams, they said, and feasting on nostalgia. It was time they put away the past and recognized their responsibilities in the real world. It was during one such conversation over the telephone that Miss Kovak came in to Cooper's office and told him he had a long-distance telephone call on the other line.

"I'll bet it's Jack," he groaned to Lucy. "And I'll bet he cancels cold. I'll call you back."

But it wasn't Jack at all. It was Kitty, calling from the hospital.

"Thank you for the flowers," she said. "They're absolutely lovely."

"How do you feel?" Cooper asked.

"Fine. Perfectly fine. Never better."

"That's great, Kitty."

"In fact, I just want you to know that I'm still planning to come up."

"Your husband said you couldn't do it."

"Well, my *husband* was wrong. It's my life. Not his. I said I'd be there. And I'll be there. Period." She sounded strangely serious, for Kitty.

"I'm delighted, Kitty," said Cooper and they said goodbye.

137

Well then, of course Cooper called Lucy immediately. She left work, and so did he, and they both dashed back to her house to discuss it. It was a warm day, her window was open, and Betsy Hoyt, who was raking leaves just down the street, heard all sorts of strange whoops and shrieks coming from Lucy's bedroom. She even called her up on the telephone and asked whether everything was all right.

"Just fine," Lucy said in a rather husky voice. "Cooper's here, and we're involved in some very exciting preparations for the Snow Ball."

"That's wonderful," said Betsy, and it was.

14

After Kitty and Jack won the dance contest at her coming-out party, they danced together all the time. They danced at the remaining parties in June, and at the ones that cropped up in September, and of course at the great chunk of Christmas parties. It was as if some spell had been broken, some secret ban had been lifted, and now at last they could dance whenever they wanted.

They danced in the summer, too. When Kitty went off to Northeast Harbor, she invited Jack to visit. He had to work on construction to pay for his college, but one Friday night in August he borrowed his uncle's car and drove all night, all the way to Maine, just to be with Kitty. It happened that that was the weekend of the Yacht Club dance, so they even danced there, although Jack hadn't had any sleep at all. In fact, they stole the thunder from whomever had won the sailing races and were awarded a special prize, before Jack had to drive back to Buffalo the next day.

And they danced on into the fall. After Jack went off to Harvard and Kitty to Briarcliffe Junior College, they still managed to get together and dance. Kitty came east to the Lowell House introductory get-together, and they danced there, and Jack went west to the Briarcliffe freshman mixer, and they danced again. They were asked to dance at the Fence Club after the Yale-Princeton game, and they did an encore at the Totem Pole in Wellesley after the Harvard-Brown. Every weekend they could, they got together and danced.

They achieved something of a reputation, at least east of the Mississippi. People began to talk about them and say they knew them, even if they really didn't. There were a number of collegiate celebrities in those days, whose names, or nicknames, were bandied about the circuit: Billy Teague, who gained more yardage for Dartmouth than any other halfback since the game was played; Redbush McPhee, from Vassar and Lake Forest, who was reputed to put out on pool tables in the cellars of fraternities; Long-Dong Hathaway, from Pennsylvania, whose fame was obvious from his name; Punch Perkins, from Williams, who could improvise dirty limericks at the drop of a hat; and Jack Daley and Kitty Price, from Harvard and Briarcliffe, respectively, who danced.

There was considerable speculation about whether they shacked up together. They moved so well together, it was natural to assume that they'd be spectacular in the sack. Nobody knew for sure. When they saw each other on weekends, Jack always seemed to sleep on some couch in some dorm, or else Kitty would have an aunt on Beacon Hill or a cousin in New Canaan, who would put her up. At least, that's what they said, but those were sly old times, and if you were discreet about it and played your cards right, there were always ways of getting together and screwing like bunnies. So who knows? Maybe they screwed and maybe they didn't. Maybe dancing did for Jack and Kitty what screwing did for everyone else.

In any case, they came home Christmas vacation and danced some more. They became a kind of punctuation for a party, the exclamation mark at the end of the sentence. People wouldn't want to go home until after Jack and Kitty had danced. And Jack and Kitty wouldn't dance with each other until the end of the evening. Which created suspense. And was also very practical. After all, life had to go on. The great swirl of changing partners had to continue. And who would dare cut in on Kitty while she was dancing with Jack? And who else would Jack want to dance with, once he was dancing with Kitty? So there was an unwritten rule that all the boys could dance with Kitty, and Jack would cut in on all the girls, for a good part of the evening.

And then would come the witching hour, along about one-thirty or two A.M., when there'd be a signal from the father who was paying for the party, and a drum roll from the orchestra, and everyone would back away off the dance floor, and whoever was then dancing with Jack or Kitty would shrug and say "Thanks a lot, anyway," and let them go, and Jack and Kitty would be left out there alone. And then, almost inevitably, Kitty would roll her eyes, as if to say, "Jeez Louise. Not again. Lemme outa here," and Jack would adjust his tie, pull down the jacket of his tux, and walk over to her with his wonderful, loose, jaunty saunter and determined direct gaze, and then he'd bow and hold out his arms, and she'd maybe give a sad little sigh and look over her shoulder at the crowd behind her, as if she were saying, "O.K. You asked for it. Don't blame *me* if I make a mess of things," and they'd dance. Then after they'd finished, the orchestra would swing immediately into "Goodnight, Sweetheart," and then people could get their coats and go home.

Of course, the season reached a climax and a conclusion at the Snow Ball. That, supposedly, was what all the other parties led up to. The Snow Ball was to put a lid on things until the new season began the following June. It was scheduled to occur two or three days after Christmas, normally on a Friday, but it took almost a whole year to organize and arrange.

No one was quite clear about the origins of the Snow Ball. It was obviously an old custom. You could read references to it—sometimes known as "The Snowflake Ball" or "The Crystal Cotillion"—in clippings from old newspapers dating as far back as the 1890s. It had occurred on and off, at various places and at various times, on up through the twenties and thirties until World War II, when naturally it had to be suspended.

Mrs. Foster was responsible for reviving it after the war. She formed a committee and put the whole thing back together. She remembered a particular party she had been to in the late twenties, when she was younger and richer, and she used that as a base to build on. But she also consulted a number of other people and did several days' research in the Grosvenor Library. She even had lunch with old Mrs. Parminter and Crazy Jane Dole, who could remember way back, and picked their brains. She also called a friend who lived in

Rochester and found out what they were doing *there*. The result was the Snow Ball as Cooper and Liz and Jack and Kitty knew it.

The central element was the election of the Snow Queen. All the girls who had come out, who had given parties, were supposed to get together down at the George Washington the afternoon before and select one of their group. Even people who had only given luncheons or teas had as much of a vote as people who had given major bashes. It was a very egalitarian system. Mrs. Foster, who managed the election, never quite made it clear what the criteria for the Snow Queen actually were. Was she to be the prettiest? The most popular? The best dancer? Or all of the above? That was never quite made clear.

In any case, the Queen would then be crowned at the Ball that night, and after that, she was to dance with her father, and then her escort, and then everyone else could dance, and the party would go on. The following day, at a reasonable hour, everyone would pile into cars and set out for Stowe and Bromley and Tremblant where they'd ski and drink beer and neck at the Round Hearth or the Bear's Den or the Boar's Tooth before settling into the second semester at college.

If the Snow Ball was the last party of the season, it normally wasn't the best. In the first place, you had to pay to get in. It was given for charity—the General Hospital, the Crippled Children's Guild, the Maria Love Convalescent Fund, something—and so you had to buy tickets of admission and even pay for your own drinks after you got there. People's grandmothers normally staked them to the tickets, but the drinks were a different story. You had to buy little chits for

143

them, which meant standing in line twice, first for the chits, then for the drinks, and if you got stuck with a girl who drank a lot, a man could be out five or ten bucks before he knew what hit him.

So the Snow Ball was a tricky proposition. Ostensibly, it was the fanciest party of them all, taking place in the gorgeous old mirrored ballroom of the George Washington, recapitulating the past glories of Mr. Van Dam and dancing school, summarizing the season, displaying the upper reaches of Buffalo society in all its colors. Which, in this case, were primarily black and white, since all the girls had to trot out their white coming-out dresses and all the boys wore black dinner jackets or tails. (There were, of course, splashes of sumptuous color around the perimeter of the dance floor, where the parents and grandparents took tables.) But the point was that the Snow Ball tended to promise more than it delivered.

One thing sure, everyone went public, so to speak. Photographers from both newspapers scooted around with flash bulbs. It made everyone somewhat self-conscious. And maybe that was the trouble. Maybe because people had been to so many parties by the time it rolled around, maybe because the boys had to pay for their drinks and the girls had to wear the dresses they had worn before, maybe the bloom was simply off the rose. Also, getting *at* it was a slight problem. You had to go through the lobby of the hotel in your evening clothes, and by then things had become a little sleazy. You'd be stared at by itinerant salesmen and prostitutes and drunks as you crossed the shabby old rugs and mounted the stained marble stairs to the sad old ballroom. It was a little embarrassing, a little silly. The Snow Ball, if truth be told, was really something of a drag.

* * *

"Who's going to be the Snow Queen?" Cooper's mother asked him, as he staggered into the kitchen at noon for some breakfast, after having been out at still another party the night before.

"Mrumph," said Cooper, poking around the refrigerator.

"What? I didn't hear you. Speak more clearly, please."

"I'm thinking," said Cooper.

"Do you think it will be Kitty?" His mother settled down at the kitchen table, watching him eat his shredded wheat, making sure he had a decent breakfast, since these were hectic times and he needed constant "fortifying."

Cooper doubted it very much.

"Why not?"

"I just don't think she will be, Mom."

He didn't want to get into it, but the reason he thought she wouldn't be was that few of the girls liked her, really, when you got right down to it. You could tell. In the first place, she had been away to school, and that automatically made her snobby and aloof. Besides, even when they got to know her, they thought she was too rich, too pretty, too casual, and occasionally too cruel. She made cracks at people. When Missy Satterfield got up at an all-girls luncheon at the Garret Club and announced she had just been pinned to a junior at Tufts, Kitty said, "Big deal," and gave a low Bronx cheer, and Missy felt silly and stupid. And this vacation, particularly, she'd been a little too blasé. She'd skipped several of the luncheons and teas without even writing notes of apology. Some people went so far as to suggest that she was spending her daylight hours shacking up with Jack in the Maid-of-the-Mist Motel down by Niagara Falls. If that was the case, then she was an immoral person and shouldn't even be elected a lady in waiting.

145

Cooper told his mother he thought Lucy Dunbar would be elected Snow Queen. Lord knows she wanted to be. She took the whole thing very seriously and was always talking about it, and now that Doctor Meisburger had fixed her teeth, she looked quite pretty. Or else Liz might be elected. All the girls liked Liz, even though she argued a lot. She was solid and dependable and chairman of the Debating Society at the Buffalo Seminary and a charter member of One World. It would be right to give it to Lucy or Liz. In any case, not Kitty. No.

But Cooper was wrong. Kitty was elected. Finally. It took three ballots in the upstairs ladies lounge of the George Washington Hotel the afternoon before, but Kitty came out the winner. Lucy was one of two runners-up, and Liz got honorable mention, but Kitty was it. Some kind of ultimate generosity of the feminine spirit must have prevailed in the clinch. Kitty was the loveliest, the classiest, and the funniest of them all, and they must have decided that afternoon to admit it.

So along about midnight, after everyone had arrived from the various dinner parties, and before the older people started to yawn and look at their watches and go home, the Snow Ball orchestra played a fancy fanfare, and the mirrored doors at one end of the ballroom swung open, and there was Kitty, looking particularly gorgeous in her white strapless evening dress, wearing a rhinestone crown and carrying a great spray of flowers, sitting in a rather tacky white plywood and cardboard "sleigh," which had once been in the window of Hodge Florists before Mrs. Foster bought it and spruced it up. Sitting opposite Kitty, and somewhat lower down, were her two ladies in waiting, Lucy Dunbar and Mary Morey, with no crowns and smaller bunches of flowers.

There were great cheers and clappings from the multitude at this vision of Kitty, and then Mrs. Foster, who was half hidden behind the mirrored door, began signaling frantically, and six boys came forward and took hold of six white ropes which were attached to the front of the sleigh and began to drag the thing, which was fitted out with small wheels, into the room. Everyone continued to clap, and the dowagers at the tables beamed and checked the jewels on their quivery bosoms, and the orchestra sawed away at "Winter Wonderland" or some tune like that.

"Prance! Prance!" called Mrs. Foster to the boys from her hiding place. "You're supposed to be reindeer!" She had selected them on the basis of their leadership qualities, and she was counting on them coming through, even though there had been only one quick rehearsal that afternoon after the election. Jack, of course, was one of them because he was president of his class at Nichols. Wally Butcher was one because he was strong and could be depended on to pull. And Cooper was one too, not because he was much of a leader, but because his grandmother had bought six tickets and took a table every year.

Slowly around the dance floor the procession went, the boys doing their best to prance as they lugged this shaky, rather ratty old float, occasionally having to dig in their heels and haul back on their lines to prevent it from careening into one of the tables and knocking over a row of glittering old ladies, while Kitty and her two attendants held tight to the sides and tried to keep their balance. Kitty, as usual, rolled her eyes and occasionally winked at people, as if to say

147

"What dopey thing will they think of next?" Below her, Lucy and Mary beamed at the multitude, tears of pride glistening in their eyes, and waved, when they could, their white gloved hands at their mummies and daddies, as a cluster of amazed waiters and maids peeked in at the kitchen door, and the stag line brooded disconsolately at the bar.

Italians haul statues of the Virgin through the streets of Siena, and on the other side of the world, Japanese youths stagger around Yokohama under the teetering burden of some huge Buddhist icon. There's no reason at all, therefore, why people in Buffalo, New York, shouldn't have devised their own secular pageant to celebrate the beauty and innocence of their women. In any case, you could tell from the cheering and applause that everyone took the whole thing very seriously indeed, except for Kitty, who was at least amused by it. Jack, of course, hauling on his rope, trying to prance, ordering the other reindeer into line, occasionally looking over his shoulder in pride and wonder at his Queen, took it most seriously of all.

The sleigh was supposed to stop in the center of the floor, and indeed it did. There was a last lurch, and Lucy momentarily lost her balance, but the thing did come to a halt. The orchestra played another fanfare, and then the fathers of the Queen and the ladies in waiting left their tables and came to help their daughters down. (Actually, it was Mary Morey's uncle who did the honors for her, since her father had been killed in the war.) After another round of applause, the orchestra struck up *The Blue Danube Waltz*, and fathers, natural or substitute, danced with their daughters while the reindeer eased the float out through the kitchen doors, to be dismantled and stored in the cellar of Trinity Church until the following year.

Mrs. Foster had instructed Jack and the others to make it snappy, to come right back and cut in on the girls almost immediately, as no girl wants to dance with her father indefinitely, and it was important to get the ball rolling again. So back they came. Cooper cut in on Lucy, and Endicott Platt cut in on Mary Morey, but where was Jack? In the confusion he seemed to have disappeared. Kitty's father continued dancing with her, and no one knew quite what to do about it, since it was so much expected that Jack would be taking over. Then the music stopped, and all things were made manifest.

There was Jack, on the raised podium for the orchestra, moving among the musicians, handing out an arrangement which they were placing on their stands. He had a short discussion with the drummer, and another with the brass section, and a careful conference with the conductor, who nodded and patted him on the back. Then just as people were beginning to wonder what was going on, the drummer went into a long drum roll. The dancers started moving off the floor, thinking there would be some sort of announcement. Not at all. Instead, all the lights in the entire ballroom suddenly went out except for two bright, slightly pink spotlights, coming from two little balconies, high up at either end of the room. One of them trained on Jack, still standing on the podium. The other hit Kitty, now standing on the sidelines with her father.

The drum roll continued. Jack, followed by his light, leapt gracefully from the stage and crossed the floor with his sauntering lope till he got to Kitty. He gave her his deep bow, and she responded with her ironic curtsy. Her father, blinking in the lights and obviously perplexed, backed into the dark. Then Jack offered Kitty his arm and led her out into the cen-

ter of the floor. The drum roll stopped. There was a pause.
The orchestra launched into the introductory bars of "From
This Moment On." Kitty gave a quick hoist to her strapless
dress. And once again they danced.

Of course, by then it was obvious what had been going on.
They had prepared a special "number." That's what they had
been doing during Christmas vacation—rehearsing. They
hadn't been shacking up at the Maid-of-the-Mist Motel at all!
People learned later that they had been working out their
steps to a special arrangement done by a friend of Jack's, who
majored in music out at the university, and who had been
playing the piano for them in Kitty's rumpus room on
Delaware Avenue, five hours a day, Monday through Friday,
till they got things right. Kitty had spent her Christmas
money on getting the arrangement copied for a fourteen
piece orchestra, which is what Jack handed out to the musicians that night.

So they danced. It was an impressive number. Jack had
worked out the choreography pretty much on his own, and
you could see the influences of Fred Astaire and Gene Kelly,
but somehow he made it seem unique and special. It began
with Cole Porter's bouncy fox trot, and then modulated into
a beguine beat, and then other exotic South American
rhythms—the spotlights both shifting to a moody blue when
they got to the tango. And then, as the beat and the lights
changed once again, they were suddenly tap-dancing! Or at
least Jack was. He had changed into tap shoes while Kitty
was dancing with her father, and now he was circling around
her, doing a series of really rather impressive tap com-
binations. And Kitty was at least pretending to respond in
kind. She lifted her dress to her knees, and wiggled her lovely

legs, and shuffled around as best she could, always ironically, always a little late, sometimes glancing quizzically at her feet as if to say *"Behave,* you two! Get *with* it please," and sometimes looking at Jack, as if to say, "You got me into this, now for God's sake get me out!"

At the end of their number, the music modulated into a fast, swing waltz, and the spotlights produced some kind of glittery effect, and the couple twirled out through the kitchen doors, which were held open by two waiters whom Jack had dealt with earlier that day.

Well, of course there was tremendous applause and even more when they burst out of the kitchen for bows, Jack swinging Kitty out to the end of his arm for a series of deep curtsies to all sides of the room. Then they even did a short encore, which Jack announced as a "Van Dam special," and the orchestra apparently had music for that, too. They bounced around the floor in a kind of a parody of all the old steps that Mr. Van Dam had once taught, mimicking the stiff, awkward motions of young people trying to learn. It was very funny. And then they topped even that by going into one final long romantic twirl, which became a kind of tribute to Van Dam as well.

The room went wild, the applause was deafening, they brought down the house, all that. And they won the Gertrude Palmer Cup, which had been kept in a special glass case in the Trophy Room at the Saturn Club since it first was awarded in 1912, and which would be returned there after Jaffe's Jewelers had engraved their names on it. Mrs. Foster presented it to Jack with a nervous little speech, and Jack beamed and handed it to Kitty, who pretended to drink out of it and then shook it upside-down as if she were disappointed that it was empty. Everyone laughed.

All that happened. But something else happened, too. Cooper and Liz, standing on the sidelines, both sensed it, though it was almost impossible to put into words. But it seemed that there, that night, some kind of a line had been drawn, separating Jack and Kitty from everyone else. Jack was no longer that nice Irish boy from over by the Peace Bridge who wanted to join the group, and Kitty was no longer the Snow Queen, the queen bee, the group's last, best hope. They had both become suddenly—what? Dancers. Hoofers. People who worked at what they did. There was something excessive about their number that night, and something vulgar too. The shifting spotlights, the soupy or-chestrations, the fact they exited and reentered through the *kitchen*, all that changed things considerably. People sensed it in their bones. Even as they clapped and shouted for another encore, they felt they were at a nightclub, applauding a floor show, rather than at the annual ball where they celebrated themselves. So when the orchestra started up again and the general dancing resumed, everyone felt awkward and self-conscious and amateur, and the Snow Ball broke up earlier than usual.

And the next day it was all over town that Kitty had an-nounced to her parents, that very morning, that she and Jack were both planning to leave college, even in the middle of the year, and turn pro.

15

Right in the middle of Thanksgiving dinner, just as Cooper had finally gotten around to carving a piece of turkey for himself, the telephone rang. Two of his children, temporarily home from here and there, leapt from their chairs, thinking of course it was for one of them. But it wasn't. It was for Cooper.

"It sounds like long distance," said his son, who had answered it.

"You'd think on Thanksgiving . . . " said Liz.

"Maybe it's someone who wants to buy a house," said Cooper, putting down his napkin and getting up. "Remember that's what puts the bread on the table." And he went to the phone.

There was a hoarse male voice on the other end, "We don't know each other, but I'm Baldwin Hall."

153

Cooper's mind was on his family so he didn't click.

"I'm married to Kitty," the voice went on, after a pause.

"Ah," said Cooper.

"I'm sure I'm interrupting your turkey, but I discover I have to fly north on Monday, and I'd like very much to stop by Buffalo and see you."

"See me?"

"I've found a plane that arrives at noon, and another that goes on to New York at two forty-five. Could we meet for lunch?"

"I suppose we could," said Cooper. "Will Kitty be with you?"

"Kitty knows nothing about this," said Baldwin Hall. "And I don't want her to know."

"Well, I'll meet your plane," said Cooper, and they hung up.

"Who was that?" asked Liz, as he settled back down at the table. The children were already helping themselves to seconds at the sideboard.

Cooper told her. "I'll bet he's going to try to pull Kitty out of the Snow Ball."

"I don't blame him," said Liz. "The poor thing's just been in the hospital and now has to come all the way up here over Christmas."

"She wants to come, Liz."

"Well, he doesn't want her to," said Liz.

"Who? What? What Snow Ball? Who's Kitty?" asked the children, between mouthfuls.

"Oh, your father's gotten all wound up about this stupid dance," said Liz.

"It's not stupid at all," said Cooper, and he tried to tell his children the whole story. He started with dancing school, then brought in Jack and Kitty, the coming-out parties, and the old Snow Ball. But by the time he'd gotten to the Downtown Rehabilitation Committee, they were through dessert and more interested in watching the football game than hearing any more on this particular topic. So he let them leave the table and settle around the TV.

"You see?" said Liz, as she started to clear the dishes. "Nobody cares anymore. You're beating a dead dog."

"We'll see," said Cooper.

"Well, all I know is that stupid Snow Ball has ruined our Thanksgiving and probably will ruin our Christmas, and I don't blame Kitty's poor husband for trying to put the kibosh on the whole thing."

And that's about all they said to each other the rest of that day.

As for Baldwin Hall, he looked pretty much the way Cooper expected him to look when he met him at the Buffalo International Airport the next Monday. He was about sixty-five and well dressed, in a tweedy sort of way. He was also portly and quite bald, and he had a red face, from the sun, or liquor, or both. Cooper thought there was enough time to take him in to the Saturn Club for lunch.

"So this is mecca," Baldwin said, looking out at the dilapidated buildings brooding over the sunken spur of the thruway which took them into town.

"Mecca?"

"To Kitty, at least. It's all she talks about these days."

"She's never come back," said Cooper.

"She wants to now."

155

"We're all very excited about that."

"I'm not," said Baldwin Hall.

They inched onto Main Street, now torn asunder by the construction of a new subway, built on federal funds for no good reason, designed to go nowhere to nowhere fast. Along each side were boarded up store-fronts, relieved occasionally by pizza joints and laundromats and hole-in-the wall food stores, along with many signs saying "For Sale or Rent. Dunlop, Potter and Jones."

"Hmmm," said Baldwin Hall.

"This isn't the good part," said Cooper.

The good part was the Saturn Club. Baldwin seemed more at home in the baronial atmosphere, and ordered a double vodka martini. Cooper had Perrier. After all, it was a working day. He was pretty sure that Baldwin wanted to make some kind of deal, and he wanted to be on his toes.

"Tell me," said Baldwin, after a sizeable slug of his drink. "This Snow Ball thing. How definite is it?"

"Very definite," said Cooper.

"Sometimes these things don't materialize," said Baldwin.

"This will. The invitations are at the printer's. People have signed up for tables. The orchestra is hired."

Baldwin sighed, shook his head, drank his drink.

"Oh, look," said Cooper. "It's just a dance. She'll be gone for a couple of days, period. Let her do it. Come yourself. Why not?"

"She's not very well," said Baldwin Hall, and then he started to cry.

Cooper wasn't quite sure what to do. It was a little embarrassing. There were several people at nearby tables who were beginning to glance over, wondering what was going on, wondering who this strange, red-faced out-of-towner was, wiping his eyes, blowing his nose, shaking his tweed shoulders.

"Oh. Hey. Please," said Cooper. "Would you like to go somewhere? We have a lounge. We have a library which is never used. Or we could go sit in the car."

"I'm all right," said Baldwin, giving his large red nose one last honk and shaking his head. He looked like a sad old spaniel coming out of the water. "I'm fine now. I'd like another one of these, if I may." He tapped his glass.

Cooper ordered him another drink, and a club sandwich for each of them while the waiter was still there, and Baldwin told him about Kitty.

It was an awkward subject for him to discuss, health. A woman's health. He spoke very uneasily. Cooper managed to discover that her session in the hospital turned out not to have been a minor operation after all. They had discovered—problems. They had—removed things. Now she was supposed to have rests, have tests, take pills, all that, but she refused.

"She's heard you can lose your hair," said Baldwin Hall. "She's heard you can feel miserable. She won't even think about any of that until after the Snow Ball." Again he shook his head like an old dog. "She's—in difficulty," he said.

"Boy," said Cooper.

"And she's a difficult woman." Baldwin gained steam. "She wants to leave her family, her friends, and risk her life just to come up here in the dead of winter and dance around a room with some fellow she hasn't seen for thirty years. I can't get over it. I can't make it out."

Cooper gestured to a waiter. "I believe I will have a drink

157

after all," he said, ordering a Bloody Mary. "Would you like a repair?"

Baldwin shook his head, wiped his eyes, and pushed away his glass. He seemed to be getting ready to do business.

"I'll try to find some way of getting her off the hook," said Cooper. "I'll call Jack. Get him to cancel. Something."

"No," said Baldwin.

"No?"

"She'd never forgive either one of us."

"Well, then look. All she need do is a few steps really. Just a bow and spin. And then we'll get her right back on the plane."

"She wants to do the whole thing," said Baldwin Hall.

"The whole thing?"

"Everything she did at the old Snow Ball."

"Good God," said Cooper.

"That's what she wants. She's dug out the old arrangement, and she's found some man who plays the piano, and she's practicing the whole damn number every day."

"Oh, my Lord," said Cooper, downing his Bloody Mary. "But what about Jack?"

"She thinks he'll practice too."

"But he's a busy man. He has a campaign. He won't have time."

"Tell him to find time," said Baldwin Hall. He took a thick envelope out of his breast pocket. "I made Xerox copies of the music. Send him a set so he can practice. And here's another for the orchestra so they'll know what they're doing. She thinks they should get together and rehearse on the afternoon of the party so she plans to arrive here early that day."

158

"That's going to cost money," said Cooper. "Orchestrations, rehearsals . . . "

"Send me the bill," he said, and got up. "And now I'd better get back out to the airport." He started out of the dining room.

Cooper grabbed the copies of the music and trotted after him. He felt a little dizzy. Too much news, too much Bloody Mary.

"Tell Kitty I'll do my best," he said as they were putting on their coats.

"I'll tell her nothing at all," said Baldwin Hall.

"But surely she expects . . . "

"She expects it to come from him. She thinks I simply went to New York."

They got in the car and started for the airport.

"May I tell Jack about Kitty's health?" asked Cooper.

Baldwin Hall turned in his seat and stared at him. "We have just had luncheon at your club, sir. I assume that everything we discussed was strictly confidential. You may simply tell the man that he'd better be good."

As they drove along, Cooper had to concentrate very hard on his driving. He felt drunk as a skunk, for some reason, while Baldwin Hall, sitting stiffly beside him, eyes straight ahead, seemed sober as a judge.

16

After Jack and Kitty won the Gertrude Palmer Cup at the old Snow Ball and announced to their respective families that they planned to turn pro, there was serious trouble in both households for the remainder of Christmas vacation. Cooper got a blow by blow description later on.

Kitty made her announcement at the breakfast table. She waited until her mother had gone to do her Saturday morning telephoning and her father had finished perusing the financial pages, and then she brought it up. She said she wasn't doing very well at Briarcliffe anyway and hated all her courses with a vengeance, except for possibly History of Art I. She and Jack, she went on, had already been approached by a theatrical agent, a man who booked acts for the Town Casino and Chez Ami, and he told them he could virtually guarantee three weeks to start with in each of these two local

161

nightclubs, and then a spring tour in various other places hither and yon. For example, he had feelers from Harrisburg, Pennsylvania, and Columbus, Ohio, where they'd go on immediately after the Jewish comedian. He promised them two hundred and sixty dollars a week, each, of which he'd take only ten percent, so she'd be earning her own keep—"which you've always said was a good experience, Daddy!" If they clicked, they could end up on Broadway or in Hollywood, and if they didn't, she swore she'd go straight back to Briarcliffe and take History of Art II.

Kitty's father threw down his newspaper and said it was the stupidest idea he'd ever heard. No daughter of his was going to be seen prancing around some nightclub, and she'd better get that into her head right now. Furthermore, he was extremely disappointed in Jack, frankly, for countenancing such a harebrained scheme. He thought they'd done a lot for Jack over the past few years, he considered Jack a kind of second son, in fact, and here he was suddenly showing his true colors.

Kitty's mother stopped her telephoning when she heard the row going on in the dining room and came in to find out what was going on. When she heard Kitty's proposal, she dismissed it out of hand. "You obviously haven't been getting enough sleep," she said. "You're all wound up, and this dancing thing has gone to your head." When Kitty tried to argue that dancing was good exercise and an extremely healthy way to make a living—"and you're always talking about health, Mummy"—Kitty's mother said she wouldn't dignify that remark with an answer. If Kitty thought for one minute that she would be allowed to leave that lovely college, and travel around the country with a man she's not married to, and live in miserable cheap hotels, and associate with sleazy unattractive people, well, she had another thought coming, that's all.

"And you're not going to dance at the Town Casino, either," she continued, "in front of a bunch of drunken salesmen from North Tonawanda. It's out of the question, Kitty, and that's that."

So Kitty's parents joined ranks, and even the maid pouring the coffee clucked disapprovingly, and finally Kitty ran from the room in tears.

Jack had similar difficulties with his parents. They were naturally proud he was at Harvard and doing so well, particularly since he was the first member of the family to go beyond high school. To leave, to give it up, after he had worked so hard to get there, was simply beyond their comprehension. His mother automatically clutched her rosary, and begged him at least to talk it over with the priest. His father fumed with anger, and then exploded.

"This is what happens," he roared, "when you quit the company of good Catholic boys and start galavanting around with the rich girls over on Delaware Avenue. Dancing for a living? What are you, a pansy these days?"

Jack's mother sighed that she had a second cousin who once made a living in vaudeville, but the poor man had been fresh off the boat and couldn't get another job for love or money.

"You quit college and I'll beat the shit out of you," said Jack's father grabbing him by his shirt, and it looked for a minute as if they were actually going to fight, except that

Jack's mother started screaming and praying, and the land-lord, who lived in the flat upstairs, began pounding on the floor.

Later, after Jack's father had gone to work, Mrs. Feeny, a neighbor, came over for coffee and the subject came up again. "Do your dancing on your own time, dear," said Mrs. Feeny. "Stick in college while you can. Otherwise, you'll lose your deferment and be sent to Korea like my boy Dan." Which was pretty good advice.

Kitty and her parents were at loggerheads all weekend, un-til finally things were resolved by a sort of compromise. All right, she didn't have to go back to Briarcliffe, despite the fact that her father had already paid the tuition for the second semester. She obviously was in no shape to make any kind of academic effort, and they'd see if they could get some kind of rebate. But she couldn't go dancing in nightclubs, either, nor could she just sit around the house and complain. So what they proposed instead was that she go over to Florence as soon as they could book passage on a decent boat, and stay at that same pension where Weezie Waterfield stayed. Lots of other attractive American girls went there, and she could study art and have a wonderful time, and in the late spring her parents would come over and they'd take a trip together, and then sit down and discuss things again, rationally, like civilized human beings.

They invited Jack over for a cocktail and expressed these thoughts to him as well. They said they really were rather disappointed he'd consider throwing away such a promising career. If he and Kitty were serious about each other, fine and good, but surely they could extend their horizons beyond the dance floor. Kitty's trip would put some distance and perspective between them, and who knows how they might feel about each other in six months time?

Jack listened carefully, fixing them with his direct gaze, and then nodded, got up, shook hands, and said he hoped they were right. He and Kitty left to meet Cooper and Liz over at The Place for hamburgers and beer. Kitty was heartbroken, and Jack was thoroughly depressed, but what could they do? You can't go completely against your parents, and even if you did, there was this goddam Korean War. You don't get a deferment for dancing. They all shook their heads sadly. Life was tough, the world was sick, parents were cruel. They all understood *Romeo and Juliet* much better now, boy, that was for sure.

So Jack would go back to Harvard, and Kitty would go off to Florence, and they'd get back together in June anyway. They'd be with each other then, and dance whenever they could, and maybe they'd be discovered by a Broadway producer.

"The theater's fine," Kitty said. "Mummy loves the theater. She knows Katharine Cornell. She might even like it if we were in something like *Brigadoon* for a while."

"Right," said Jack. "We'll show 'em. We'll dance up a storm at all the parties all next year."

"If you're invited," said Liz.

"Why wouldn't we be?" asked Jack.

"Because we're old now. We're out. We're on the shelf. They'll be asking a whole new crowd."

"Then we'll crash," said Kitty. "We'll crash every party and dance anyway."

"Or we'll hire ourselves out," said Jack. "Like the Whiffenpoofs."

"Exactly," said Kitty. "Or like that sweet little man who does cartoon caricatures. We'll make up a brochure of what we do, and ask Mrs. Foster to mail it out to everyone planning a party."

"Righto," said Jack. But you could tell they were both whistling in the dark.

Cooper and Liz kept in touch with both of them over the next year, Cooper at Brown, Liz at Smith. Those were the days when everyone wrote a lot more letters than people do now, and there was a genuine pleasure in seeing your college mailbox darkened by the shadow of something more than a bill. Besides, since people met all the time at football games and hockey tournaments and in Bermuda in the spring, there was a rather sensitive network of information which shivered like a spider web when something new was added. So Cooper particularly kept up with Jack and Kitty and knew, or could guess, pretty much what was going on.

Back at Harvard, for example, Jack threw himself into his work. Since he couldn't dance with Kitty, he seemed to have all sorts of energy for everything else. He joined a posh club—Signet, Porcellian, one of those—and waited on tables so he could afford the dues. He ran for office in his class, and was elected secretary despite the Andover–Exeter bloc which voted for someone else. He maintained at least a B average in all his courses and captained the freshman baseball team, as well as playing intramural volleyball and squash. He even played a respectable Hotspur in the Lowell House production of *Henry IV, Part I*. He soon became known as a wheel in several categories.

He and Kitty wrote to each other twice a week, then once a week, then once in a while. Jack's letters were precise and neat, like little compositions, with topic sentences and subordinate clauses and precise conclusions. They didn't sound like Jack at all. Kitty's responses from Florence, on the other hand, were lazy, sometimes illegible scrawls. She hated to write and was the first one to admit it. From her letters, Jack deciphered that she missed him terribly, that Florence was cold and rainy, and that the Italian men kept pinching her rear end. The light was so bad in the art galleries that you couldn't see the paintings even if you wanted to. Oh, well, she wrote, it will all be over in June.

Her parents arrived in early May and whisked her off to Greece. That was where she met Bradley Read, from West Hartford and Yale, who was over there serving as an admiral's aide in the Sixth Fleet. Kitty's parents knew his parents, so maybe they knew he'd be there. In any case, they looked him up and asked him out to dinner at the King George Hotel. Afterwards, Kitty and Brad took a taxi to the Acropolis and walked up to the Parthenon, and of course it was perfectly beautiful. Later that week, Brad had them all to lunch on his aircraft carrier which was moored right there in the Bay of Salamis, off Piraeus, where the Greeks had defeated the Persians two thousand years before. How could Kitty fight all of that? The glory that was Greece, the grandeur that was the USS *Coral Sea*, the big rush from this handsome naval officer in his whites, and her parents right there, constantly commenting, constantly encouraging, like a built-in Greek chorus. By the end of the week she had written Jack a letter which, after he had deciphered it, seemed to say she had fallen in love with someone else.

It was close to exam time at Harvard, but what the hell? Jack borrowed a total of eight hundred dollars from his rich friends and flew to Athens as soon as his passport came through. He had a series of awkward and contorted conversations with Kitty, but nothing much was accomplished. There, amid the crowded streets and hectic Mediterranean atmosphere, they found it difficult to connect. Kitty's parents were cold and polite, and very smartly stayed out of it.

Jack, too, took Kitty up to look at the Parthenon by night, but that didn't help much either. All she seemed to see was the lights of the fleet, beckoning in the bay. Maybe things would have been different if an orchestra had struck up a tune and they had danced. But there was no orchestra on the Acropolis. No orchestra anywhere, except occasional little combos in the main square churning out exotic Greek music with strange and variable rhythms. Mr. Van Dam had never taught them how to dance the bouzouki.

After a week Jack decided to fly home. Kitty kissed him good-bye at the airport and there were tears in her eyes. Jack turned and gave her one, last, long, direct look before he ducked into the plane. That was that.

That summer, Jack got a job through his roommate in the oil rigs out near Tulsa, Oklahoma, so that he could pay back his friends for their loans. He wasn't around for any of the parties. Neither was Kitty, who spent most of her time visiting Brad at his family's summer home in Norfolk, Connecticut. She announced her engagement that fall, and they were married in Trinity Church the following June. The reception was out at Kitty's grandmother's house in East Aurora, where her coming-out party had been, the year before.

Jack was invited, of course, but of course he didn't come. "Thank God," Kitty's mother whispered to Cooper as he came through the reception line. "Suppose he had arrived and wanted to dance with the bride."

17

DUNLOP, POTTER, AND JONES
Real Estate and Insurance
Serving Buffalo for over 100 years.

Dec. 3, 1983

The Honorable John X. Daley
Lieutenant Governor
The State House,
Indianapolis, Indiana
46200

Dear Jack:

Enclosed is a copy of the old sheet music you and Kitty used when you danced at the Snow Ball. Someone dug it up, and I thought it might interest you. As a matter of fact, have you considered repeating your old number? I'll bet you still remember it, Jack! And I'll bet Kitty would be willing, if you are. I could get the music to the band ahead of time, and you and Kitty would probably only have to rehearse a couple of hours during the afternoon, right before the ball. It should all come right back. Just do what comes naturally.

Let me know if this is even a remote possibility, and I'll alert Kitty.

I hope all goes well with your campaign.

Best,
/s/Cooper
Cooper Jones
Vice-president

There was no answer from Jack during the next week, so finally Cooper put in a telephone call to Jack's office. Mrs. Windkoff got on and said that Jack was in Washington, at a Republican National Committee meeting. She remembered Cooper's letter, of course, but had no idea how the Lieutenant Governor intended to respond to it. Cooper left word that Jack should call as soon as he could. After all, they were getting down to the wire.

A few days later, the telephone rang at a quarter to eleven in the evening at Cooper's house. Liz was already in bed, and Cooper was trying to make up a Christmas list from the L. L. Bean catalogue. He was sure it would be Jack as he picked up the receiver.

"This is Joan Daley," said a woman's voice at the other end.

"Joan?"

"Jack's wife."

"Ah."

Liz came sleepily downstairs in her nightgown, rubbing her

eyes. "If that's one of the children, tell them it's much too late to call."

"It's Jack's wife," said Cooper.

"Well, it's still too late," said Liz, but she sat on the stairs to listen.

"Is it too late to call?" Joan Daley said.

"Oh, no, no."

"Actually I've been out on the campaign trail for Jack. You get used to late hours." She had a brisk, clear way of talking.

"I see."

"It's a crucial campaign. He's trying to pin down the nomination in March."

"I hear."

"Yes, well, what I'm calling about is I have to fly to New York this week, and I wonder if I could stop in Buffalo on the way back. I'd like to meet you."

"That would be fine."

"I've heard so much about you from Jack, and I just think it's very important we touch base, or cross swords, or whatever."

"Of course," said Cooper.

She named the day and the time, and they said good-bye and hung up.

"Good for her," said Liz, after Cooper had told her what went on.

"Why do you say that?"

"Well, I imagine she thinks this whole thing is as stupid as I do. Only she has guts enough to do something about it."

She turned and went back upstairs to bed. Cooper watched her go. He wondered whether she knew about Lucy. He also wondered, as he watched her figure, silhouetted

171

through her nightgown by the upstairs hall light, if it was too late now to make love. But then he began to wonder about Joan Daley, and Jack and Kitty, and so he sat downstairs for another hour.

Cooper took Lucy with him when he met Joan Daley at the airport. He thought it was important that they deal with her as a committee. She obviously couldn't be terribly happy about the idea of Jack dancing with Kitty, and Lucy might be able to give her sisterly reassurance.

She was easily recognizable as she came through the gate. Brisk, trim, well gotten up, slightly tan as all politicians and their wives seem to be, she determinedly scanned the crowd clustered at the gate as if she were looking for someone carrying a sign, and then bore down on Cooper and Liz, and greeted them almost before they had the chance to greet her.

"I just have time for a quick drink," she said, already clipping down the vast, slick corridor in her high heels, and banking into the bar as if she were on automatic pilot. She was a woman at home in airports.

So they sat and ordered drinks and talked, over by the big bay window where planes came and went behind them. She chatted breezily about politics and about how actively she was involved in Jack's career. She seemed very knowledgeable about precincts and counties and various votes. She also managed, in a very short time, to drop all sorts of information about her five children, who seemed to be attending every first-rate school and college in the country.

In short, she was the ideal candidate's wife. Cooper could see her on the family Christmas card, perched on a couch,

172

hands in her lap, knees locked together, Jack standing stalwartly behind her, five bright, brushed children displayed around her, and a gorgeous golden retriever panting uneasily at her feet.

Of course, as he watched her, Cooper noticed a few chinks in her armor. The neat hair, fresh from the hairdresser, was faintly reddish, slyly dyed, he thought, or looked that way in the gaudy airport light. And the clothes were too obvious, too square, too color-coordinated, with her neat little initials on the lapel of her jacket. And there was something faintly genteel about what she ordered—piña colada—and how she held her glass. And much too much name dropping about who she knew in politics. You could tell she had her nose pressed slightly to the glass. She had the drive and energy and alertness of those on the outside eager to get in. She was smart and hungry and eager for success, a perfect complement to Jack.

So they talked, and she really was very good at bringing them out. ("Tell me about Buffalo. Jack says it was a lovely old city. . . . I want to hear about your children. How many do you have, and what do they do?") But with her second piña colada, she began to zero in on the real point of the visit.

"This Snow Ball thing," she said. "Is it all set? I mean is it really definite?"

"Oh, sure," said Cooper.

"Oh, gosh yes," said Lucy.

Joan Daley frowned very briefly and then flashed a bright smile. "Sounds like a fun evening. Very quaint. Very nostalgic."

173

"Let's hope," said Cooper.

"It's more than that," said Lucy. "It symbolizes the rebirth of downtown Buffalo."

"How nice," said Joan. "Will the media be there? Photographers? Television? Any of that?"

"I imagine so," said Cooper. "It's a story, after all. The old ballroom, two old friends getting together and dancing . . ."

"Suppose I danced with him," said Joan Daley.

There was a pause. Cooper glanced at Lucy.

"I hope you will," he said.

"No, I mean instead of her."

"Oh, but that wouldn't be the same," said Lucy.

"No, it wouldn't," said Joan, with a sweet smile. "It would be quite different. But actually, we're not bad together. I mean, sometimes we dance at various functions. We've— we've done the twist."

Cooper felt a little cornered. "I think it would be great if you did the twist. Just fine. But I hope he'll still dance the main dance with Kitty."

"I'm the main dance, mister," she said.

"Well, I know you are, of course, but you see, there's Kitty."

"Screw Kitty," he could have sworn he heard her say, under her breath.

"What?" said Cooper.

"I'm his *wife*," said Joan. "He should be dancing with me!" She smiled sweetly again. "I don't think it's a good idea for a man who expects to be nominated and elected governor of a large state to be dancing on television with a woman who's not his wife. I don't think that's a good idea at all, do you?"

She started groping angrily in her purse. For a moment

174

Cooper thought she was looking for a gun. Finally she produced a crumpled pack of cigarettes, and after a furtive glance around the room, lit one—snap, with a brisk little lighter—and began puffing away rather furiously.

"It's just two old friends," said Lucy.

Joan didn't seem to hear her. "He's practicing now," she said, shaking her head. "He's cancelled two big speaking engagements just so he can go out in the garage and practice dancing. He's set up one of the kid's tape decks, and he's got some woman from the Y coming over to help him out, and I mean who are we kidding? I want you people to get on the telephone first thing tomorrow and tell him to cool it, will you please? He can dance. O.K. He can even do a little number, off camera, with this Kitty. But when it comes to magic time, he dances with me."

"I can't tell him that," said Cooper.

"It won't *mean* anything," said Lucy. "It's just a fun thing."

"You tell that to the unemployed steelworkers in Gary when they see him on the tube, tritty-trotting around the room with some eastern society type. You tell the farmers downstate after they lost thirty percent of their crops last fall. Tell them it's just a fun thing. Honey, it'll mean votes, that's what it'll mean. It'll mean the urban vote. And the farm vote." She paused. "And maybe my vote too."

"What do you mean?" said Cooper.

"I didn't shake all those hands and sit through all those speeches so I could end up on the sidelines watching my husband throw it away," she said, and got up. "No. Sorry. Change the format, or I'm not coming. Which will look bad. And I might not be there when he gets back. Which will look worse. And when the dust settles, I might even run for

175

something myself in a couple of years. Now where the hell's the ladies room, please?"

Cooper started to point it out and Lucy offered to accompany her, but she shook them both off and found it on her own. They waited for her outside uneasily.

"Maybe we can still butter her up," said Lucy.

"How do you butter up an armadillo?" said Cooper.

Finally she emerged, all combed and all smiles.

"What a pleasant airport," she said. "What interesting decor. Is it close to town?"

They walked down the corridor toward security. She turned before she went through, and held out her hand. "Thank you so much for a pleasant afternoon," she said. "It's been a very fruitful discussion all around, and I think we've all learned a good deal. Good-bye. Good-bye." Then she turned to the woman at the security belt. "Here. I imagine you'd like to have my purse."

As she went through the metal detector, Cooper half expected all sorts of buzzers and alarms to go off. But none did, and she turned and smiled and waved a white-gloved hand before she disappeared down whatever those corridors in airports are called.

"Poor Jack," said Cooper to Lucy, as they drove back to town.

"Why poor Jack?"

"Married to that."

"I sort of admire her," said Lucy.

"Why, for God's sake?"

"For knowing what she wants. For sticking to her guns. For insisting that Jack make up his mind."

"Hmmm," said Cooper. They drove on in silence for a while.

"I think *you* should make up your mind, too," Lucy said suddenly.

"About what?"

"About me and Liz."

"Oh, God, Lucy."

"I do. I think you should sit down with Liz and have this whole thing out on the table."

"Now, now."

"I think you should, Cooper. Maybe I'm old-fashioned, but I think you should bring things to a boil."

"Give me time, Lucy."

"I'll give you up to the Snow Ball. If you haven't told her by then, then I will."

Cooper didn't reply. They drove on in silence toward the city, toward the George Washington Hotel which Cooper could now see half hidden behind the new buildings, outlined against the darkening winter sky.

18

For several years after Jack and Kitty won the Gertrude Palmer Cup, the Snow Ball continued on as an annual event. Other couples won the cup, but they didn't dance half as well as Jack and Kitty. Snow Queens were pronounced to be "almost as lovely as Kitty Price," and their various partners might seem to move "a little like Jack," but it was not the same thing, and everyone knew it. Even the awarding of the cup became a little sentimental or a little corrupt. One year Sophie Stuntz won it just for navigating around the floor after her bout with polio, and another year they gave it to Peter Palmieri and his partner, whoever she was, because his father had donated a new wing for the hospital. Sometimes people hoped Jack and Kitty might come back just as guests, just as visitors, just to show the younger people how it was done, but of course they were long since gone by then. After a while the Snow Ball was abandoned as extravagant and impractical. The coming-out parties died away. Jack and Kitty's dancing became a vague oral tradition, a piece of local trivia, an occasional recollection for those who knew and cared.

Years passed. Times changed. The elms died. Buffalo suddenly looked old, naked, and embarrassed. "The Queen City of the Great Lakes," "The Gateway to the Future" now became known as "The Mistake on the Lake." Industries began to close down or move away. Ships from the St. Lawrence Seaway could be seen in the distance, their smoke trailing over the horizon, bypassing the harbor on their way to Cleveland and Detroit. A branch of the new thruway slashed cruelly through Delaware Park, destroying its Olmstead design. The Catholic cathedral, built of imported white Carrara marble, cracked in the cold and was torn down. The Erlanger Theatre was razed into a parking lot. Kitty's grandmother's house was sold to the Knights of Columbus, who sold it to the Jewish Community Center, who sold it to an organization for cancer research. One third of the population fled to the suburbs, to the southwest, to wherever.

Cooper and Liz were married three years after Kitty married Bradley Read. Cooper had served his stint in the Navy and Liz had tried living in New York, working for a travel agent. They asked both Jack and Kitty to the wedding, but neither could come.

"Would that we could," wrote Kitty in a note accompanying a lovely Steuben bowl. "But we can't."

Cooper even telephoned her to try to persuade her. But no.

"You can't go home again," she sighed, and made it seem as if no one had said it before.

As for Jack, he was hopelessly incommunicado, working in a lumber camp out west, saving money for law school that fall.

Cooper and Liz started having babies almost immediately. After their third was born, they wrote Jack and asked him to be the godfather. Jack was taking his bar exams by then, so he couldn't make it, but he telephoned to congratulate them.

"You ought to convert to the true church," Jack said. "Three in three years?"

"We think we've discovered what's causing it," said Cooper.

By then Cooper had bought the old Babcock house on Middlesex Road and had gone to work for his father. He and Liz threw themselves wholeheartedly into parenthood. They adored their children and sometimes, in the evening, would miss them so much that they'd go upstairs and wake them up just to be with them again.

On Saturday nights, they'd get together with a few of their friends to drink liquor, eat casseroles by candlelight, and talk about schools. By ten o'clock, they'd start to yawn and worry about the baby sitter and so start their good-byes. They all knew each other from Mr. Van Dam's, but nobody did much about dancing. They were too tired for that.

As they grew older, those who remained in town hung on jauntily, enjoying what echoes and memories there were of the old coherencies. They hunkered down at their clubs, paying ever increasing dues with ever diminishing dividends from inherited securities. They bought old wine, new tennis racquets, and better burglar alarms. The men went into stockbroking and banking and estate management. The women ran little boutiques, or sold furniture from old estates

181

on consignment, or became social workers and tried to prop up the families of the poor even as their own were falling apart. The maids and cleaning women and yard men died, or retired, or priced themselves out of business. It was all very sad.

Meanwhile, Jack and Kitty had changed too. The word would come back from time to time, the grapevines would tremble and shake, and people kept some sort of tabs on them both. There were still Christmas cards, after all, and occasional get-togethers for lunch or dinner when either of them came to town to see their families, and occasional chance meetings in airports or resorts. So it was possible to piece together some picture of their separate lives.

Jack, for example. Everyone knew he had had some sort of difficulty at Harvard his last two years. Something to do with booze. Some people said he was trying to drown his sorrows after losing Kitty. Others said it was simply the age old Irish malady. Whatever it was, it led to a few fights in Cambridge bars and a few incompleted courses and a couple of raucous incidents at Smith and Vassar. By his senior year, he had pulled himself together enough to graduate and join the Marine Officers Training Program at Paris Island.

There his old leadership qualities had reemerged. All right, so he couldn't lead Kitty around the dance floor anymore. He did lead a platoon of forty marines up some grimly numbered hill in Korea, and won a Distinguished Service Medal for doing it. And if his undergraduate grades prevented him from getting into the Harvard Law School after he was mustered out, he still got into Georgetown, which he attended on the G. I. Bill of Rights, and where he led his class.

He also led his roommate's sister, Joan O'Hara, down the garden path, so to speak, and when she became pregnant, he was man enough to lead her down the aisle.

They had a small wedding at the Church of Our Lady of the Perpetual Sorrows in Indianapolis, where Joan's father happened to be County Commissioner or something. Jack's mother and father went, of course, but nobody else from Buffalo was able to make it. "We're not having ushers and bridesmaids and stuff, but I hope you'll come," Jack wrote Cooper. But they couldn't. It was just too far, and no one knew Joan. They sent a salad bowl from the Savoy Shop and a telegram, and that was that.

Kitty wasn't invited. When she heard about it later —through Lovey Dunn who just happened to see her on the tennis courts at Harbor Island—she burst into tears, but that could have been because she was already in the throes of her first divorce.

Jack's father-in-law got him a job at a law firm in Indianapolis at a starting salary almost equal to what they'd offer a graduate from Harvard. He was bright and competent on the house closings and wills and divorce settlements, and before long he was involved in politics, at least at the local level.

He ran first for precinct chairman, and then for the city council, and then for the state legislature. He was described in various editorials as a liberal Republican with Democratic instincts. He spoke passionately about more jobs and better schools and decent trash pickup. As usual, his charm and energy served him well. And as usual, he managed to touch all the bases: there he was, on posters and mailings, surrounded by his beaming, burgeoning family; there he was, on

183

the six o'clock news, his arm around some ballplayer or bricklayer, regaling him with his Irish wit; there he was—in a photograph not for publication—on the terrace of the country club, enjoying a gin and tonic after a golf game with a friend of a friend of a friend he had known back in Buffalo.

He ran for this and he ran for that, and as soon as he won, he made plans to run again. It seemed that he liked running more than what he was running for. He loved the hectic schedules, the anonymous press of the crowds, the ritual phrases, the ritual applause. At a victory celebration in the vast dining room of some noisy hotel, he would trot out Joan and his family with a pride that seemed immensely real: five children now blinking uneasily in the light, three boys glistening with Clearasil and two daughters with clamped smiles to hide their braces, marched briskly onto the platform by Joan, with her fixed hair and fixed grin and watchful uneasy eyes, all to be bussed and hugged and squeezed with heartfelt tenderness by a man they hardly ever saw.

So that was how Jack got to be Lieutenant Governor of the great state of Indiana, and how he was going to be Governor too. And there was no reason to think that things would stop there. Already he was being mentioned in occasional local newspaper columns as a senatorial candidate in the nineties, and *Newsweek* listed him among twenty other "young Republican hopefuls" who were bringing fresh blood to the party.

Cooper saw him only occasionally, when he came to Buffalo to visit his parents. Jack never let him know ahead of time. It was as if he didn't want to be seen. But once he did call, at about six-thirty in the evening.

"We're just about to have dinner," said Cooper. "Come on

184

over. There's plenty of food and you can meet the kids."

"Can't," said Jack. "Got to hang out with the old folks at home."

He did want to meet afterwards. At the Shamrock Bar, for some reason, on the west side. Cooper showed up at around nine-thirty, already yawning and wondering how long he'd have to stick around. Jack was at a corner table, downing beer and holding court with a gang of his old cronies from Holy Angels. They were giving him hell about being Republican. Cooper had a better time than he thought he would, and by midnight, when everyone else was calling it quits, Jack persuaded him to drive out to a place called the Club Moonglow on Niagara Street, where they could hear some jazz. "There's always been good jazz in this town," Jack said. "Few people know it." He was right too, and between sets they talked about the old days. Jack, with careful off-handedness, brought the subject around to Kitty, and Cooper told him what he knew.

By two in the morning Jack was really quite loaded. A couple of women came to their table and asked them to buy drinks. One of them already knew Jack from somewhere and said, "Long time no see." Cooper decided it was time to go home, but not Jack.

"You go on," he said. "I'll get home by myself. I'm serious." Cooper could tell that he was. As he was putting on his coat, Cooper glanced back and saw the women settling in at Jack's table, and Jack putting his arms around them both.

But that was Buffalo, and only occasionally, and for the most part Jack stayed in Indiana and furthered his career. Did he ever dance? Oh, once in a while you might hear that he'd done a turn or two with Joan at some inaugural ball, or a few impromptu shakes with a secretary or companion at some disco in New York when he was out on the town, but that was about it. Apparently he tried to waltz with his daughter at her graduation from Meadowbrook Country Day, but she had never been to dancing school and had no idea how to follow his lead, so they stumbled, waved apologetically at whoever was watching, and quickly sat down. No one out there, not even Joan, knew what a good dancer he really was.

On the other hand, you could say that he danced all the time. He bowed deferentially to the abortion issue. He held his arms out to nuclear disarmament. He did a series of elegant dips and turns on the Middle East. He sidestepped the budget issue, did a lovely reversal on school busing, and marched a firm, solid line against the Vietnam War. You'd have to say that he danced well. He was serious, earnest, and intense. He looked a subject in the eye, took hold of it, and led it where he thought it ought to go. What was missing then? What was wrong? Why did people go away from his speeches feeling vaguely dissatisfied? His jokes were there in the right places, his facts were solid and carefully researched, his solutions were forthcoming. But still he lacked irony, disengagement, something. He was too dead-on.

Columnists and commentators would occasionally struggle with the problem: "What is his overall vision?" they'd ask. "Where is his center? Does he have more than a laundry list, a catalogue of improvements?" These questions were raised now and again with no answers provided.

Once, on a television talk show, when Jack and all the other candidates were sitting around some sleek formica coffee table discussing the issues, the moderator asked him pointblank, "What do you really *want*, Mr. Daley? If you had your ultimate druthers, what would you really like to have happen?"

Well, it was a tough question, no doubt about that, but Jack had no idea what to do with it. It must have opened some strange doors in him. He sat there, staring at his interrogator for what seemed like an intolerably long time. There was a silence, an emptiness, a darkness which seemed to spill out of every television set that was tuned in. Roger Bliss, who was in Indianapolis at the time taking his children to the auto races and happened to be watching it at the Holiday Inn, said it was a creepy moment indeed.

"Maybe what he really wants is to dance with Kitty," said Cooper to Liz, when he heard about the incident. "Maybe he just couldn't say it on the air."

"I hope he wants more out of life than *that*," said Liz, thumbing impatiently through a professional journal.

Anyway, Jack didn't say it on television, and soon the other candidates leapt in and started talking prison reform and acid rain and the Equal Rights Amendment, and before long Jack was right in there pitching with the best of them.

In any case, Jack had been elected and appointed and reelected and reappointed to any position he set his sights on. And rightly so, most people felt. He worked hard, did his homework, spoke intelligently on the issues, and conveyed a sense of confidence and charm. The odds were he'd make a very good governor. Carol Graham, who married a man from Indianapolis, wrote Lucy in her Christmas card that she certainly intended to vote for him. "He's the best we have," she said.

187

19

And what about Kitty? What happened to her? If Jack was born to lead, she seemed born to follow. She followed her parents' suggestion that she go to Florence, join them in Greece, marry Brad Read. When his ship was sent back abroad , she followed him there. She followed the fleet as it steamed majestically around the Mediterranean, spraying its planes out to the far reaches of the old boundaries of the Roman Empire, displaying its power, making sure the Free World stayed free. The great gray ships would barrel into the shimmering blue harbors of Gilbraltar, Cannes, Beirut, Naples, and sooner or later, there would be Kitty, perched on a pier, waiting for Brad to come ashore. When he was transferred to shore duty in Charleston, she showed up there, and when he was mustered out in time to enter Harvard Business School, she followed him there as well.

Why then did they get divorced? What was the trouble? Nobody seemed to know. From all reports, they were having a wonderful time in the Boston area. They rented a lovely little carriage house in Lincoln and unpacked the sumptuous wedding presents which had been in storage in Buffalo. They got an adorable Lab puppy named Dusty, and their neighbors had a horse which they begged Kitty to ride. They made a lot of new friends and reconnected with a lot of old ones, and they'd go skiing with the gang at Cannon Mountain in the winter or sailing in the summer on Martha's Vineyard. Brad was doing extremely well at the B School, and Kitty and a friend were runners-up in the ladies doubles tennis tournament for the entire Lincoln-Weston-Wayland area. They would have won except that Kitty was slow in following her serve to the net.

But still they split up. It was strange. After graduation, Brad accepted a good middle-management position at a bank in San Francisco and flew out to look for a house. Kitty was supposed to stay behind and supervise the moving. He found a house—a sweet one, apparently, in Palo Alto, with even a pool—and made a deposit on it, but suddenly Kitty refused to go. "Come on!" he shouted, calling her across the country just as he must have called her up the trail on Mount Washington or into the great waves at Nauset Beach on Cape Cod. "Come on!" But she wouldn't come. And no one knew why.

It wasn't that she preferred Boston. She packed up and left soon after the divorce. And it wasn't even that she hated California. When she married again, she lived willingly in L.A., which is a lot more California than San Francisco ever thought of being. So what was it?

Lucy Dunbar put the question to her six months after the divorce when they were having lunch in New York before a matinee of the Lunts in *The Great Sebastians*, which Kitty particularly wanted to see.

"I hate to pry," said Lucy, "and if it's none of my business, tell me to shut up. But what the heck happened? I mean, there he was, sitting in San Francisco . . . "

"I couldn't follow him," said Kitty, and signaled for the bill.

After the play, she said enthusiastically, "Did you notice how they both talked at the same time, and yet never interrupted each other?"

"Sort of," said Lucy, who was disappointed in the afternoon.

"That's why they can't play with anyone else," said Kitty. "And that's why I divorced Brad." And then she had to leave.

Brad never talked about it either. He was very gentlemanly about the whole thing. He even offered to pay alimony, which Kitty refused because she had plenty of money— though it later turned out that she didn't have quite as much as she thought.

Years later, Ted Greber and his second wife met Brad and *his* second on some golf course near Tucson. Afterwards they had cocktails together, and apparently there was a genial and benign discussion of first wives. "Kitty was terribly late," Brad told Ted, who brought it back to Buffalo. "Late for everything. She never wanted to be anywhere else from where she was. You had to drag her around. You can tell a lot about a woman by her attitude toward time." But that's all he told about Kitty.

Kitty's second husband—Dirk Detweiler was his name —was late, too. Chronically late, compulsively late, according to those who met him. Well, people thought, at least they can be late together. He came from California—Balboa,

Malibu, San Bernardino—anyway, one of those places that lie in the sun around Los Angeles. And that's where he took her to live.

"He's very laid back," said Lucy, who visited them once in the mid-sixties. "We all sat around endlessly, and nobody made a move about dinner until at least quarter past ten, and I had to sleep on some lumpy old couch. But I think Kitty's happy. Or seems to be."

Kitty met Dirk on the chair lift at Aspen, where she was skiing with friends. He was a part-time ski instructor and a waiter at one of the lodges. He liked to stand outside the regular lift line and then ride up with a pretty girl if she happened to be alone. Kitty was certainly one of the prettiest on the mountain. Sleek, tan, trim, packed into her ski clothes as if they grew on her, she drew attention wherever she went. Dirk almost had a fight with somebody else who wanted to ride up with her too, but he won out and slid into the seat beside her.

Before they had even reached the halfway mark, he was offering her private lessons at a special rate. "Follow me," he said when they reached the top, and she tried to, all the way down. She wasn't a bad skier, but her lazy, linked turns were pretty much out of date. Dirk offered to show her how to cut over the tops of the moguls and do a series of sharp, fishtailing wedlens right down the fall line.

"Gulp," said Kitty. "Well, I'll try."

But of course she couldn't learn. Couldn't, wouldn't, didn't. She'd ski after him, all right, but she'd glide languidly back and forth across the mountain, like some vague afterthought to his passionate plunge down the center line. Finally she'd ease herself onto a ridge, take off her cap, toss her hair in the sun, and say, as he climbed back up to get her, "I'm hopeless. I'm a lost cause. You should go play with someone your own age." (She was five years older than he was, and knew it.)

Most of this information came from the Littlefields, who were out there on an extended vacation trying to patch up their own marriage. They reported that when the people with whom Kitty had arrived wanted to leave, she thought she'd stay on a few more days. And did, checking out of her hotel room and moving into Dirk's van, which he kept in a parking lot over at Glenwood Springs.

She stayed with him all winter. Her skiing didn't improve much, but her disposition did. She and Dirk were fun to be with around the bar after the lifts closed, and fun to have dinner with, and fun to hang out with afterwards. They'd dance occasionally too, at the discotheques, but of course you couldn't see how good a dancer Kitty could be when she was wearing warm-up pants and those clodhopping boots.

She also found a job while she was out in Aspen. On the upper reaches of the Puma trail, as she was easing into one of her casual, noncommittal reversals and probably muttering to herself, "Ooof. Ugh. Isn't it against the law to do U-turns around here?" a fashion photographer took her picture, and when he developed it, he was so impressed with how she looked that he offered her a job modeling ski togs for the posh shops in Aspen village. So Kitty posed all over the place, and for the next year or so you'd find her picture in snappy catalogues and once in the *New York Times Magazine*. "Hey, isn't this Kitty Price in this fur job here?" people would say, and it was. But even though the pictures came out a year later, Kitty's job didn't even last through the winter. She kept being late for her appointments, and when she finally showed up, the light would be wrong and the assistants ready to quit. So that ended that.

Dirk decided to pick up stakes after the spring skiing. He packed up his van—now loaded with odd dishes and silverware from the various lodges where he had been a waiter—and drove off to Los Angeles. Kitty moved to a motel, thought about it for a few days, and then followed. She sold her General Motors and DuPont stock in order to buy one of those strange houses that sit on stilts out there in the hills. There they lived. Dirk, who was a good carpenter, advertised himself in the Los Angeles *Free Press* as a "Home Design Consultant," which meant he put in kitchens, and Kitty grew vegetables in their garden and did volunteer work for the L.A.A.S.P.C.A.

Lucy Dunbar visited them later on. The book store she worked for had been bought out by Walden, and now she had to go to a book fair in Los Angeles. "A *book* fair? In Los *Angeles?*" people exclaimed, but that's where it was, so she went. While she was out there, she thought she'd look up Kitty. She thought she might be tough to track down, but lo and behold, there she was in the Hollywood telephone book, listed under her maiden name.

"Lucy! Egad! A voice from the past!" Kitty shrieked into the telephone. "Where *are* you? What hotel? Don't move a muscle. I'll come and get you immediately and we can all catch up!"

She showed up a couple of hours later in a battered Karmann Ghia with torn seats and an overloaded ashtray. They almost ran out of gas on the Santa Monica Freeway, but managed to coast off into a gas station. Kitty had forgotten her purse, so Lucy paid for a full tank and a new fan belt, since the old one was about to go. When they got to Kitty's house, things were somewhat in disrepair because Dirk was in the process of adding on a sun room, but they cleared a place, drank beer, and talked about home. Dirk showed up sooner or later and produced a bottle of gin, so they switched to that. After the three of them were pleasantly polluted, Kitty got up, swayed a little, and announced she planned to do something about dinner. Dirk and Lucy got up too, and said they'd help, so they all staggered into the kitchen. Kitty opened the refrigerator door and stared inside for a good long time. Then she said, "Oh, the hell with it," and they all went out to eat Chinese food. Again, both Kitty and Dirk had forgotten their money, so Lucy treated them, and afterwards it seemed awfully late to drive all the way back to Lucy's hotel.

"You can sleep right here," Kitty said, brushing the sawdust off the couch and laying down a torn sheet. Lucy had a rough night because of the lumpy couch, and because Kitty and Dirk broke their bed about 3:00 A.M.

"I must say they seem to have gotten it all together in *that* department," said Lucy later, at home.

In the morning, she read a book until Dirk appeared in his underwear and produced some old corn flakes and instant coffee. He was to take Lucy back to her hotel because it was right on the way to where he was working. After he got a neighbor to help jump-start his car, he woke up Kitty, who came outside in her bathrobe to kiss everybody good-bye.

"Go tell the Spartans," she said to Lucy.

"Tell them *what*, Kitty?"

"Tell them . . . Er. Uh. Tell them I'm alive, at least."

195

Later, on the Freeway, Dirk said casually that they were thinking of getting married.

"That's great," said Lucy.

"Thinking about it," said Dirk. "She might be having a baby."

"Wonderful," said Lucy.

"*Might* be. We're not sure. At least she's a little late."

Kitty's second marriage lasted about six years all told, which was twice as long as her first. The baby—a girl named Melanie—was said to be adorable, and Dirk finally finished the sun room, but still, things didn't really work out.

"Maybe we were too much alike," Kitty told someone later. "Things were terrific in bed and all that, but I don't know ... we weren't getting anywhere." Apparently they consulted a marriage counselor who nodded knowingly and said they had a problem in cross-fertilization. "I don't know about that," Kitty said. "I do know that there were times when I felt as if I were married to myself."

Anyway, they split up and sold the house—for not very much, actually, since by then it was kind of a wreck. Dirk moved in with a man.

"Kitty! You poor thing!" said Lucy, when Kitty called her and told her this on the telephone.

"Don't be silly," said Kitty. "He's a nice man. If he had asked me, I would have moved in with him myself."

Kitty was calling all her old friends because she had decided to move back.

"I want to return to my roots," she said. "I yearn for the style and structure of the decadent East."

"Why don't you come back to Buffalo?" Lucy said.

"Um. That might be overdoing it," said Kitty.

Eventually she rented a garage apartment in Greenwich, Connecticut. She had several friends from Ethel Walker's and Briarcliffe who lived there now, and they recommended the good grocery stores, and a good day school for Melanie, and some good projects for herself. They also gave several small dinner parties where she might meet more men.

And of course she did. She was still rather gorgeous to look at, if now a little bit plump, and tremendous fun to be with, with her vague smile and scattered thoughts and odd way of being slightly out of sync with the rest of the world. Men wanted to take care of her, and several did, but she finally married Baldwin Hall, who was the uncle, actually, of Wiggy Smith, whom she had known in the old summers at Northeast Harbor.

Baldwin was trim and spry for a man of sixty-three, and he taught her how to play good golf and a decent game of bridge. He had a large house with a lovely pool on a point of land at Key Largo, in a resort called Ocean Reef. You could sit by the pool and watch the sun go down every night over cocktails, except on the nights when they sprayed for bugs, when you had to go inside. Kitty and Baldwin decided to live there permanently, except for the really hot summer months when they'd go to Baldwin's old family camp in the Adirondacks, and watch the sun go down there.

Florida worked out fine for Kitty. She seemed very happy. The Boococks saw her there, and so did the Pomeroys, when they stopped in from that cruise of the Bahamas.

She asked about Buffalo. "How are things in Lower Slobovia?" she said.

"It sounds like a crack, but it wasn't," Dottie Boocock said later. "Not the way she said it. I think she really misses us."

Anyway, Florida seemed to be working out very well. Kitty's daughter came down from boarding school over vacations, and Baldwin's children, with their children, came down a lot too. They all adored Kitty. She was young enough to intervene when gramps got the grumps, and vague enough so she didn't fuss about wet towels on chairs and dishes in the sink and fights over the television. She became a benign, easygoing, matriarchal figure at the age of forty.

Of course it was easy to be benign and easygoing at Ocean Reef, because they had phalanxes of black maids who were trucked through the gates before breakfast and trucked out before dark, and who took care of everything while they were there. And on their days off, you could all go over and eat at the golf club or the beach club, or the Angler's Club down the road. It was also easy to be benign and easygoing when you were mildly boozed all the time. You usually had a drink after golf or tennis and before lunch, and two before dinner. You went to a cocktail party at least four times a week, where you might even break down and have an extra vodka and tonic before you came back to eat the meal which Lou-Ellen had made that afternoon and left in the microwave oven, ready to be turned right on.

Everyone had cable television, so you could watch all sorts of wonderful programs at night—Masterpiece Theatre where they put on these wonderful English things, old movies, fantastic documentaries about animals and nature—or else you could just put your feet up and read a good book. And when you finally went to bed, the ocean breeze whispering through the house felt cool as a kiss.

And that was the life Kitty was living before she got the call to come back to Buffalo and dance at the Snow Ball.

20

And so the great day drew near. People got through Christmas, but there was none of the usual letdown afterwards, since this year the best was yet to come, two nights hence, down at the George Washington Hotel. Indeed, in many homes, around many trees, the Snow Ball became a major theme of gift giving. George Platt finally coughed up and gave his wife Mona the fur coat she had long wanted, now that she had something to wear it for. Mitzi Stockton put a set of pearl shirt studs into Norman's stocking, so that he would have no excuse for putting on a soft shirt with his dinner jacket. Bracelets and rings and necklaces, bow ties and suspenders and cummerbunds, silk socks and handkerchiefs and evening purses all were offered up in an orgy of anticipation. The Robert Potters even gave each other a new gray Honda Accord so that they could drive down to the hotel in high style, but their children racked it up Christmas night.

Delhurst Cleaners, who did by far the most careful job in town, had to hire a temporary extra presser just to keep up with the stacks of evening clothes which were thrown onto their counter, smelling of moth balls and the cedar closet. Eastman's had a sudden run on black shoes. Mabel Danahey's and Berger's had both anticipated an extra demand for long skirts and dresses, but their racks were virtually bare the week after Thanksgiving, so a number of women had to make special trips to New York on People Express.

A large number of dinner parties were planned. Several of the maids who had once served were tracked down and cornered and persuaded for huge sums to serve again. One of them was in a nursing home and had to have a special permit to be gotten out. Carolyn McAlister's daughter, Debbie, who was trying to start a gourmet catering concern, received fourteen telephone calls in three days, and Bill Paglia, the steward at the Tennis and Squash Club, got his dates mixed up and committed himself to tend bar at two parties the same night. He had to bring in his brother from Batavia.

Liz tried to stay out of all the planning, but she did point out that there were too many articles in the paper about the Snow Ball—when it was, who would be there, who was giving parties beforehand.

"We're all going to be sitting ducks," she told Cooper. "While we're all down at the George Washington, dancing our little hearts out, every burglar in Buffalo will be up in this neighborhood, robbing us blind. It happened at old Mr. Stillwell's funeral, and it will happen with the Snow Ball.

And I don't think our burglar alarms will stop them, either."

So Cooper warned everybody, and people called Burke's Security and hired house sitters for the evening and took their silver down to the bank. It really was quite a proposition, planning and going to a big fancy ball in these perilous times.

There were even difficulties about where Jack and Kitty should stay. Cooper invited Jack to stay with them, but Mrs. Windkoff wrote that "since it was now unlikely that the Lieutenant Governor's wife would be able to attend," Jack would spend the night with his widowed mother, and have dinner with her too, before the dance. "He hopes the publicity attendant on the affair will be as low-key as possible," she added. "Mr. Daley regards the event as personal, rather than political."

Mrs. Windkoff also asked Cooper to reserve some space on the afternoon of the ball where "the Lieutenant Governor might be able to practice his steps with Mrs. Hall. If the orchestra could be there, all the better." Cooper found an old dance studio in a building on Chippewa where apparently choruses from road companies of *Blossom Time* and *The Student Prince* used to rehearse when the Erlanger Theatre was in operation. He reserved that from three to five for very little money and signed up the orchestra for considerably more. And he wrote Kitty about it.

Where Kitty would stay was another problem. Her parents were dead now, and both the house on Delaware and the house in East Aurora were long since gone. Her sister was now totally gaga in a sanatorium in San Diego. Lucy wrote Kitty that she hoped she'd stay with her—"It's a small place, but mine own." But when Kitty wrote back that Baldwin had decided to come too, Lucy had serious second thoughts. They'd have to share a bathroom with her teen-age children who were hopelessly messy, and she knew that having one's own bath can be extremely important to older people. The Ralph Fenwicks had just converted the old chauffeur's apartment in their garage into a rent-producing entity. It had a lovely new bathroom and its own TV and everything. They offered it willingly, even though Grace Fenwick had never been terribly fond of Kitty. Finally Lucy decided the hell with it, she'd exile her children to the houses of various friends, even though it was Christmas vacation. Baldwin and Kitty would stay comfortably with her.

"As for the Fenwicks' garage apartment," Lucy told Cooper, "it's something to keep in mind for you and me."

"Hmmmm?" said Cooper, vaguely.

"After the Snow Ball. When we bite the bullet. When we finally tell Liz."

"Oh. Right," said Cooper.

Cooper had forgotten about that. He kept forgetting about it. Things had been going along so pleasantly, it seemed a shame to talk about biting bullets and bringing things to a boil and cutting bait and doing all those things Lucy kept saying they had to do. He enjoyed Lucy, enjoyed her seriousness and intensity, enjoyed her in bed. She was so deliciously respectable, even in the throes of passion. Everything about her—her lacy underwear, the snappy little toilet kit she brought along "to repair the damage," her decorous little squeals of delight which made him feel as if they were playing a good game of tennis or golf—appealed to him. She was dancing school incarnate, that strange old world made flesh.

And they had worked so well together. They had "put

their shoulders to the wheel," as Lucy herself put it, for almost a year now, and it had been great fun rolling the ball uphill. They were like two actors who had become involved with each other during the intense schedule of rehearsal, as their lives outside became less and less significant. They were cast in strictly supporting roles, but it was a romantic comedy after all, and they found themselves bestowing on each other some of the luminosity which emanated from the stars. "How does the subplot reflect the main plot of the play?" they used to ask Cooper when he studied English at Brown. Well, he knew now.

On the other hand, the play was about to open, and good or bad, it would last only one night. Then what? The turmoil of a divorce, followed by the Fenwicks' garage apartment with Lucy? What would they do from then on in? Listen to old musical comedy records? Read Salinger and Fitzgerald? Go to movies on Sunday afternoon, and tell people "we liked this and we didn't like that"? Be mildly irritated by each other's children? Order the same things at restaurants? Wear matching parkas and identical jogging suits? Waltz through the remainder of their days without an argument, Cooper Jones and his second wife, Lucy, a living testimonial to congenial compatibility?

Well, why not? What was so bad about that? Why did his mind keep sliding away from the issue? Did he still love Liz? He fought with her more and more. These days they managed to disagree on almost every single subject, particularly on the Snow Ball.

"It better be good, that's all I can say," said Liz one time when he was struggling over the contracts for the orchestra. "It better be terrific."

"It will be terrific if people want it to be terrific," said

203

Cooper pointedly. "It'll be just great if people give it half a chance."

"I find it kind of hard to get all wound up over some dumb dance, Cooper, when this city has an unemployment rate of just over fourteen percent."

"What about the people we're employing for this party, Liz?"

"A mere drop in the bucket."

"Civilization must go on, Liz. Otherwise there's nothing to be employed for."

"That's what the orchestra said as they tuned up on the *Titanic.*"

So it went. Another time she asked about the decorations, and he thought maybe she was becoming interested.

"Oh, well," he said, "we thought we'd concentrate on the snow motif. Crepe paper icicles, white flowers, white tablecloths, bunches of styrofoam snowballs on the tables."

"That's what I thought," she said. "Are they fireproof?"

"Oh, Jesus, Liz."

"What if people smoke? The whole thing could go up in flames."

"The stuff is all fireproofed these days."

"Oh, sure. That's what they always say. I should probably call a fire inspector."

"Stay out of it, please, Liz."

"Well at least I hope you have a smoking area, Cooper. I am not going to go to that party and have a lot of people blow smoke in my face. I think you should rope them all in, at the far end of the room."

That was the kind of thing they argued about, again and again, more and more, as the day came closer. But it wasn't as bad as it sounds. She cared. He could tell. He could tell by the way she kept bringing it up, returning to it, fighting it out. He found himself admiring her for that, even as they fought. A couple of times, after an especially heavy argument, he just had to grab her and give her a huge hug, even as she argued about *that*. She was fighter, all the way down the line. She was fighting her past, fighting her marriage, fighting the whole corrupt world she saw around her. She was strident, and intrusive, and he was sure she'd be that way until the day she died. He could see her then challenging her doctors, disagreeing with her nurses, and finally, when she got to heaven, managing to irritate the pants off God. Oh, she was an interesting woman. And even when he was angriest at her, Cooper wondered whether she might not be more fun to grow old with than Lucy, who was always saying "Exactly," "How right you are," and "I couldn't agree more."

21

The morning of the Snow Ball dawned damp and gray. Cooper, who had had trouble sleeping, got up early and took a walk around the Meadow, a lovely expanse of land emerging at the east end of Delaware Park and ending at the zoo. He thought of the drives he used to take here with his grandmother, snuggled next to her under the lap-robe in the old Pierce Arrow, as she gave orders to the chauffeur, far forward, behind glass, who would nod and tip his cap in reply.

"Go slowly, Edward," she'd say, "so we can see the buffalo. There they are. Your grandfather calls them bison, Cooper, but that's because he's thinking of that stupid baseball team. I know a buffalo when I see one. Oh, and look. There are the beavers. See their flat tails? That's how they chop down trees."

The land stretched out under its blanket of old snow,

webbed by the trails of Sunday cross-country skiers. In the
center, a great old elm which had somehow survived the
blight stood stoically against the sky. A few joggers slugged
by. A dog walker stumbled down the rutted bridle path. In
the distance, over the Lion House, heavy clouds huddled
ominously. The morning traffic, now picking up down
Delaware Avenue, sounded muffled and obscure. He knew,
without knowing he knew, as anyone from Buffalo knows,
that they were in for snow.

He had breakfast at home alone. Liz had already left for
work. He had told them at the office that he wouldn't be in
until the afternoon, so he took his time over the paper, then
got out his old black evening shoes and polished them up. He
even took a crack at ironing his cummerbund, but got into
trouble on the pleats and decided to leave that for an appeal
to Liz. At around eleven, he drove out to the Buffalo International Airport to meet Jack.

Lucy was already there, waiting for Kitty's flight from
Florida, via Atlanta, which was due in half an hour later
than Jack's. The plan was for each to meet their respective
planes, then all gather at the Saturn Club for lunch, and after they had "broken the ice," as Lucy put it, drive down to
the studio on Chippewa where the orchestra would be
waiting to rehearse.

Jack's plane arrived on time—a little early, as a matter of
fact, dropping smartly in under the clouds. Cooper had no
trouble recognizing him as he came through the gate. His
thick hair was a steely gray now, and he had gained some
weight, but the old bright-eyed, head-on gaze and beaming
smile were still very much in evidence. He bounced up to give
Cooper a strong handshake and Lucy a big kiss, even though

you could tell he wasn't quite sure who she was. He looked good, immaculately dressed in a trim tailored overcoat topped by a natty scarf, and his bag hung jauntily from one finger over his left shoulder. His bright blue eyes were set off by that ruddy complexion most Irishmen manage to acquire, and everyone in the area seemed to sense he was a celebrity even before the television news cameras appeared out of nowhere, and the microphones were poked in his face. He seemed extremely happy to be home, and said so immediately for both channels, before he had second thoughts.

"Of course now I've made my home in Indiana," he said wryly, " 'midst the fields of yellow corn." It was hard to tell whether he was serious about that or not.

"We understand you're going to dance tonight with an old flame," an interviewer asked him.

"There's no flame like an old flame," Jack answered with a grin. And then, gallantly, "Of course, I think you'd do better to refer to us both as young sparks." And then, suddenly serious. "I thought I could take time out from my responsibilities in Indianapolis in order to celebrate the rebirth of the downtown area of this equally fine city." And then, with a twinkle. "You better make sure the ambulances are waiting in the wings."

"I'm sorry about that," said Cooper, as they made their way to the front of the terminal, where his car was double parked. "I had no idea they'd show up."

"I'm used to it," said Jack.

"They'll be at the dance too," said Lucy. "We tried to discourage it, but it's a public occasion in a building involved with public funds, and I'm afraid they have every right to come in."

"It goes with the territory," said Jack.

They stood by the car. Jack hesitated and looked around.

"She's not here?" he said.

"I'm staying to meet her plane," said Lucy. "Then we'll all collect at the Saturn Club for lunch."

"Ah," said Jack, and jumped briskly into the car.

"I'm sorry your wife couldn't come," said Cooper as he started up.

"Yes, well. She sends her regrets," Jack said. "Christmas. Kids home. All that." He looked out the window.

"You were good to come yourself."

"I wouldn't miss it. Hey. Skip the Thruway. Let's drive in the old way, down Main."

He sat on the edge of his seat, one hand on the dashboard, almost like a child. Occasionally one leg would start to bounce up and down out of nervous energy. He watched the city go by with great interest. Nothing seemed to depress him. They passed the old Hewitt-Robbins factory, windows broken or boarded up, a battered Dunlop, Potter, and Jones sign hanging askew on its rusty fence. "Great old building," Jack said. "Great old architecture." They passed the Grenada movie theater, now showing *Teen-age Temptations.*

"At least they're still there," he said.

"The buildings?"

"And the temptations."

They turned onto Humboldt Parkway, now bleak and treeless under the brooding skies.

"Sad about the elms," said Cooper.

"Oh, well. It must be light and airy in the summer," Jack said. And even the ghastly desecrations along Delaware Avenue didn't phase him. "Democracy in action," he said.

"Much better than just the monotonous mansions of the rich." Buffalo could do no wrong. He looked around, bright-eyed, leg bouncing, as if he had finally arrived at the Emerald City.

"I hear Indianapolis is a great town," Cooper said. "Really up and coming. There was an article about it in *Newsweek.*"

"Oh, they're on their way," Jack said, as if all that were behind him.

They had a beer in the Grille Room at the Saturn Club, and democracy or not, Jack seemed delighted with that too. People came up and said hello, and he was buoyant and charming. He remembered many more names than you would have thought possible, and shook every hand as if he had found a long-lost friend. Once or twice, though, he took a quick look at his wristwatch, and Cooper could tell he was nervous about Kitty. Then Mrs. Leeming came in from the desk and said that Lucy had called from the airport. They were to go ahead and start eating since Kitty's plane had been delayed.

More people came up to greet him at lunch.

"Do you think you'll be the next Governor of Indiana?"

"Only when I laugh," said Jack.

"Are you nervous about tonight? Do you remember any of the old steps?"

"Oh, I've got a memory like an elephant," said Jack. "I'll probably dance like one, too."

He beamed continually, and fielded their questions aimiably, and ate his cheese omelette, and only occasionally glanced furtively at his watch.

After lunch, they decided they might as well go on down to the studio to meet the musicians. They left word at the desk for Lucy and Kitty to meet them there whenever they could.

Outside it had begun to snow. There was already an inch or so on the streets, and the driving was tricky. It was beginning to look as if they were in for a good old Buffalo blizzard. Traffic was beginning to creep northward from downtown as people left work early, but Jack and Cooper were going the other way and easily found a parking place in front of the studio.

As they climbed the creaky old stairs, they could hear a few members of the orchestra already tuning up. Jack introduced himself and shook hands all around, repeating their first names as he heard them, and then greeted the other members who were drifting in, brushing the snow off their instrument cases. He reminded Cooper of a recording star —Sinatra or someone—cozying it up with the boys. They settled into their chairs, fussing with their instruments, trying a few riffs, keeping their jackets and parkas on, since there wasn't much heat in the building.

Cooper had mailed the music to the orchestra a few weeks before, and they said they had already run through it a few times.

"So have I," said Jack. "Let's try it while we're waiting, and I'll go through the motions by myself."

But as they were about to start, they heard someone clomping hurriedly up the stairs, and in came Lucy, covered with snow. She said Kitty's plane had finally landed, but Kitty wasn't on it.

"Maybe she's chickened out," said Jack, with a nervous laugh.

"Don't be silly," said Lucy. "She wouldn't do that. Not Kitty. She's just a little late."

"Where have I heard that before?" said Jack.

"When's the next plane?" asked Cooper.

"Four-thirty," said Lucy. "If she's on it. And if it's able to *land.*"

Nobody knew quite what to do. Cooper decided to go over to his office to see if there were any messages. Lucy went home to wait by the telephone. Jack thought he'd stay in the studio and work out with the band. Cooper left him rolling up his sleeves and doing stretch exercises while the orchestra got ready.

At his office, Cooper found there had been a telephone call from Atlanta.

"Some man," Miss Kovak said.

"Did he leave a message?"

"No, but he said he'd call again."

Cooper telephoned Ocean Reef. No answer. He called home, but Liz was still at work. He called the club, called Eastern Airlines, called Lucy, but there was no word anywhere.

"I suppose it was Baldwin saying they'd missed their plane," said Lucy.

"I suppose," said Cooper. "But why didn't he say so?"

When he got back to the studio, Jack was moving around the room, dealing with the orchestra. "Now on the third bar," he was saying, "I think I'll swing over here, and bring her around with me, and then I want you horns to hit it hard." They did. It was impressive. "And here's where you modulate to the new key, so you should pick up the tempo, and-a-one-and-a-two, that's it, that's it, and then I guess I'll take her into a spin." He only half danced these things, but you could see he had some of the old grace, despite his added weight.

"O.K., that's it for now, fellas," he said. "See you later." He shook hands with several of them as they packed up, and

213

remembered more than a few names. As they left, he called after them: "Now go easy on me tonight, gang. Make me look good."

Then he came up to Cooper, buttoning his shirt and wiping his brow with his handkerchief. "Any word?"

Cooper shook his head. "Someone called, but there was no message."

"Jesus Christ. What's that supposed to mean?"

"They probably didn't have time to call again. And now they're obviously in the air somewhere. The storm is all across the East, and they've got her stacked up over some airport."

"Maybe the Good Lord's against us on this one," said Jack.

"Don't be silly," said Cooper.

Outside, the snow was already six inches deep and beginning to drift, as a blustery wind blew in off the lake. The plows and sanders were already out and around, and Cooper drove behind one as far north as he could before he peeled off to drop Jack at his house on Porter Avenue.

"Want to come in?" asked Jack halfheartedly, as he opened the door to get out.

"Better not," said Cooper. He knew Jack never liked to bring friends home. "I'll call you when we hear anything, and I'll pick you up on the way down to the ball."

"Fine," said Jack. He hoisted the bag onto his shoulder and trudged up the unshoveled walk toward the front porch of the gloomy, ramshackle, double-decker house. Cooper could see a dim light glowing vaguely through the driving snow.

214

22

One thing about Buffalo, New York. They know how to deal with snow. Storms really don't phase them very much. The plows come out, the boots go on, and life continues pretty much on time. Other cities begin to tremble at the first ominous weather reports. Before long, they're dismissing their schools and cancelling their meetings and cautioning their populace to stay indoors. Not Buffalo. It takes a major catastrophe, it takes the Blizzard of 1977, to bring her even temporarily to her knees.

This was no such elemental blizzard, the night of the Snow Ball. This was a good, solid, western New York snowstorm, the first of the winter really, and it served more to whet people's appetites than to dampen their spirits. There didn't seem to be any question that the Snow Ball would be held, as planned, down at the George Washington Hotel.

Cooper called Saul Radner just to make sure. "Are you guys going ahead with Winterfest?"

"Of course. Aren't you?"

"Sure."

"See you there."

That was it. People came home from work, maybe a little late, maybe a little early, but they took their showers and got dressed and got ready to go out.

Cooper, of course, was very worried about Kitty. Again, he called everywhere he could think of—Ocean Reef, Eastern Airlines, the Buffalo Airport—but either the lines were busy or nobody answered or nobody knew. Jack called Cooper a couple of times, and Cooper tried to be reassuring, but he had nothing to report.

"Well, if she doesn't show, I imagine my campaign manager will be delighted," said Jack. "And my wife."

"I know what you mean," said Cooper.

Cooper, of course, knew things that no one else knew about Kitty's health, and that worried him all the more. He finally put a call in to the Miami Hospital for a Kitty Hall, but there was nobody of that name registered. He was beginning to feel very depressed.

Liz arrived home from the hospital about twenty minutes late, all brisk and energized by the storm.

"It's perfectly beautiful out there," she said. "Wait till you see the trees."

Cooper was sure she'd gloat when he told her about Kitty's absence. "You see?" he thought she'd say. "You see what happens when you start messing around with the past?"

But she didn't say that at all. What she said was, "Don't worry. She'll show."

"What makes you think so?"

"I know Kitty. She'll make it. She'll get there."

They got into their evening clothes. Liz had gone out and bought a new dress—"Much against my better judgment" —and Cooper watched her standing in front of the mirror, putting on the ruby earrings she had inherited from her mother. She looked lovely. Cooper felt guilty as hell about Lucy, and discouraged about this whole damned Snow Ball. He was beginning to wish they could just stay home, have some scrambled eggs or something, light a fire in the fireplace in the bedroom, and make love.

Liz, of course, like most people who have been married a long time, slid naturally into the opposite mood. She became increasingly perky and chipper as they got ready to go.

"I must say," she said, "I'm looking forward to the evening. Just putting on these stupid clothes has gotten all the old juices going."

They were invited to the McKinleys' for dinner before the dance, and since Kitty and her husband were supposed to be there too, it soon became generally known that Kitty hadn't arrived.

"You'd think she'd at least *call*," said Sylvia McKinley. "I don't know whether to tell those creatures in the kitchen to hold dinner or not."

People clustered in groups and discussed the problem. As the cocktails flowed, there were suggestions about what to do if Kitty didn't arrive. Someone proposed that Jack do a solo, like Fred Astaire, but everyone knew he wouldn't, even if he could. Someone else suggested that they give him a substitute partner, but who should it be? Mimi Mott came to mind im-

217

mediately, since she and her ex-husband had both been to Arthur Murray's in the effort to save their marriage. Lucy Dunbar even went so far as to call her up at the Caldwell's dinner party and ask her to stand by.

"Not on your life," she said. "You won't get *me* out on that dance floor in place of Kitty Price. I'd look like a fucking fool."

Lucy returned to the party shaking her head. "I think she's had a little too much to drink," she said.

During the dessert the telephone rang, and everyone waited breathlessly while Sylvia McKinley went to answer it. When Binkie Byers started scraping his plate for his last strawberry, everyone wheeled on him and said "Sshhh!" but they couldn't hear much since the telephone was out in the hall. Finally Sylvia came back, shaking her head.

"I am very confused," she said, settling into her chair, making the most of the suspense. "Very confused indeed. That was the New York State Police."

Everyone froze. You could have heard a pin drop.

"I couldn't make head nor tail out of what he was saying. It was a very bad connection—all sorts of static—some radiophone or something—and I kept wanting to say 'Roger' and 'Wilco' and all that. But he *did* say that he had our girl and not to worry."

"Had our *girl?*" said Cooper.

"And not to worry. 'Keep the faith, baby,' he said, and then hung up, or signed off, or whatever they do." She waited until the maid had cleared the dessert dishes, and then leaned forward and whispered, "Frankly, I think he was black."

"But what the hell does it mean?" said Cooper.

"It means we keep the faith," said Liz, and then they all went into the other room to have coffee and discuss it.

It was still snowing at ten-thirty when everyone began to leave for the dance. The driving was treacherous, and the caravans of cars snaked their way through those streets which had been partially plowed, to converge in a slow stream down Delaware. Cooper veered off to pick up Jack. He honked the horn and Jack came out, his mother a brief shadow against the light behind her.

"Any news?" Jack asked, sliding into the front seat next to Liz.

Cooper told him about the call from the police. "I'm getting really pissed off, if you want to know," he said. "These cryptic messages from strange people. What is this? The Second Coming? Why didn't she call us her*self*?"

"Maybe she couldn't," said Liz.

Jack recognized Liz, and gave her a big buss, and told her how great it was to see her again.

"I think Kitty will be there, Jack," she said. "Cooper's losing faith, but I'm not."

"Either way, we're in the lap of the gods," Jack said, settling back in his seat.

They found a parking lot, somewhat plowed, and joined the crowd, stumbling in little groups along narrow improvised paths and over slippery snowdrifts toward the George Washington Hotel which stood massive, serene, and ablaze with light at the far end of the bleak expanses of the new mall. The fresh air and impending excitement did

219

nothing to penetrate Cooper's depression. As they trudged along, they all seemed to him to belong to an illustration for Dante: dark, shadowy, forlorn souls, staggering against the stinging wind toward some vain image of salvation, a Snow Ball in Hell.

Even when they had burst through the new automatic sliding glass doors into the warmth and light of the lobby, he felt strangely disconnected. Winterfest was going strong, all right. The booths and tables were in full operation, and streams of people in colored parkas swirled among them. There was a tumultuous variety of smells from the various cooking stalls, and a strange cacophony of sounds as a string quartet at one end of the space competed with a Gospel choir at the other. In his dark mood, it all seemed grotesque and absurd to Cooper: Vanity Fair, democracy run rampant, capitalism in its death throes—people buying things they didn't need, eating things they didn't like, pushing, shoving, shouting, moving from booth to booth in a frantic search for nothing in particular.

Saul and Judy Radner came up to them as they were making their way toward the stairs. They looked trim and well-dressed and proud of what was going on. Cooper introduced them to Jack.

"We'll be up later on to see you dance," Saul said.

"If it happens," said Cooper. "Kitty hasn't shown up yet."

"She will, she will," said Liz.

"Well if she doesn't, come down and join a real party," Saul said.

"I'd be glad to," said Jack, whose political instincts were fast emerging in the life all around him. Cooper could almost feel him straining at the leash, eager to move into the crowd, press the flesh, kiss the babies, eat a taco and a pizza and be photographed doing it.

They elbowed their way on. Cooper had thought they might feel a little awkward in their evening clothes, but not at all. In the vast democratic turmoil around them, where everyone seemed involved in a kind of desperate self-dramatization, they simply were wearing another costume. Indeed, at one point they were shoved aside by a group of punk rockers, who were wearing ratty cast-off tuxedos of their own.

They checked their coats and boots in the refurbished cloakrooms at the foot of the grand staircase, and after Liz took a flick at her hair with her comb, they straightened their shoulders and started up. Cooper heard Jack draw in a deep breath, and he felt his own stomach churn as in the old days. "I feel as if we were marching up to meet Mr. Van Dam," he said. Jack nodded.

"Don't be silly," Liz said. "It's entirely different. Look how much they've remodeled the building." But even *she* automatically took Cooper's arm as they climbed the stairs.

Soon they could hear the sounds of the orchestra above competing with the noise of the crowd below, and then as they came into the ballroom, the music took over. Cooper had hoped that once he was in this lovely old room, with friends and music and lights and decorations, his gloomy mood would go, but this didn't happen at all. Lots of people had already arrived, yet the party seemed glum and dispirited. The orchestra played a plaintive, desultory tune—"The Last Time I Saw Paris"—and a few people drifted sadly around the dance floor. Others were sitting morosely at

221

---

their tables, or clustered in wan little groups at the two bars, drinking sour white wine in ratty plastic cups. Lucy's decorations drooped gloomily. Off in the corner, in an old evening dress, in a new wheelchair, sat Mrs. Foster, white-haired, feeble, and unattended. Someone had brought her out of the Presbyterian nursing home especially for the occasion, and there she was, blinking out through bottle-thick glasses at the almost empty dance floor. Near her was the old sleigh from the Snow Queen ceremony, water-stained and warped, which someone had found in the cellar of Trinity Church. The Gertrude Palmer Cup was sitting on the seat, partially polished and filled with flowers, but the effect was still somewhat pathetic and forlorn, like an ill-tended altar in an abandoned church. The two television crews, which had set up their equipment earlier in the day, were now beginning to pack up to move downstairs where at least there seemed to be a little more activity.

"What have I done?" Cooper said to himself, surveying the scene. "What have I done?" The phrase kept repeating itself in his head until he realized where it came from: Alec Guiness in *The Bridge Over the River Kwai*, who said it as he recognized the futility of his labors, before he threw himself on the dynamite plunger and blew the whole damn thing to smithereens.

People were already coming up to Jack and commiserating with him about Kitty. They offered all sorts of excuses, as if he had been stood up by a date: missed connections, damned Buffalo weather, unreliable airlines. Jack rallied to the attention, remembered more names than you would have thought possible, and managed to make everyone feel much better. The die had been cast as far as he was concerned. He was to be simply a politician tonight, after all, and he warmed to the role.

The party warmed with him. He began to move from table to table, and by the time he had made it around the room, the evening seemed to have half a chance. He spoke to the bandleader and asked him to play a livelier tune—"Green-Up Time"—and as the beat picked up, he came back and asked Liz to dance.

"Oh, Jack, don't be silly. I'm hopeless," she said, but he led her onto the floor. She was stiff and self-conscious, but you could see she was trying hard, and Jack obviously still knew what he was doing, so their little turn around the floor earned a small smattering of applause from those who happened to see it.

But suddenly there was a peculiar flurry from the area of the stairs—one of those bustling disturbances that can ripple through a room—and then Lucy Dunbar burst into the ballroom, breathless, pink-cheeked, damp from the snow, still in her overcoat, and announced to left and right, like a Greek messenger, that Kitty had arrived and was changing in the ladies room right at this very moment. Then she went to the podium, got the orchestra to play a fanfare, and announced it again.

That started the ball rolling, all right. There was immediately more activity at both bars, and someone even sent up a tray of drinks to the band. Someone brought Lucy one too, and people gathered around, as she took off her coat and sank into a chair at the Danforths' table and breathlessly told her story to whoever wanted to hear.

Apparently what happened was this: Kitty and Baldwin had had to change planes in Atlanta, but as they were walking from the American to the Eastern counter, Kitty fainted. Just keeled over in the middle of the terminal. "It must have been just plain nerves," Lucy said. Well, they took her to first aid and put her on a cot, and Baldwin retrieved their baggage and called Cooper at his office to say they'd have to cancel out. Cooper wasn't there, of course, and he couldn't really leave that kind of message, and when he wanted to call again, Kitty wouldn't let him.

"She put her foot down," Lucy said, her eyes brimming. "She promised to be here, and she wasn't going to let us down. Now that's what I call good old-fashioned Wasp pluck!" She looked around at the group who was listening to her. Everyone murmured agreement.

"Aaaaanyway," said Lucy, and she went on. Apparently Kitty rose from her couch of pain with just enough time to grab another plane, but this one ran into the storm and they were forced to land at Syracuse. Immediately they tried to telephone but either everyone's line was busy or they didn't answer, so they rented a Hertz at the airport and started out through the storm. They probably were driving too fast, because they ran into a huge snowdrift outside Canandaigua. There they sat, and then of course they *couldn't* telephone. Finally the police showed up and got a towtruck to pull them out, and so on they came, this time with a police *escort*, because Kitty turned on the charm and told them about the Snow Ball. The police fell totally in love with her and radioed ahead, "so that was what *that* was all about, and now they're here, they're *here*, people," said Lucy, "and Kitty's going to dance!"

Soon Baldwin Hall appeared, looking a little rumpled in his wrinkled dinner jacket, soft shirt, and lopsided bow tie, since he had changed hurriedly in the men's room. The excitement of being there, having survived the trip, having made it after all, gave him a rather jaunty air. Someone handed him a double scotch, and as he was introduced around, he retold the story of their trip in still more elaborate detail. You would have thought he was the guest of honor himself. He was finally introduced to Jack, and they shook hands and beamed and thumped each other on the back like old friends meeting after a long time.

And then there was a contagious buzz of conversation and a clustering of people at the entrance to the room, who parted either way like a chorus in a grand opera opening up for the entrance of the prima donna, because lo and behold, there she was. There was Kitty, in a purple dress, looking lovely once again. The ballroom burst into spontaneous applause. Cooper, who was standing near Jack, heard, or thought he heard, the same low groan of longing he had heard over thirty years ago.

She waited there in the doorway and looked around, the same old Kitty with the same quizzical expression on her face, as if she were saying, "Gulp. Er. Um. How did I get myself into this one?" The television crews were already unpacking their equipment and setting up again, and a man with a hand-held camera was already moving in on her. She looked at him, and rolled her eyes heavenward, and looked at him again. Cooper could almost hear her say, "Hey! What do I do? Say cheese, or what?"

Baldwin, gallant old gentleman that he was, walked over to meet her and offered her his arm, which she took with a kind of wry amusement. People applauded again, and naturally

225

formed two lines, a kind of gauntlet, leading to Jack. Baldwin nodded to either side like royalty, Kitty smiled her vague lop-sided smile, as if she were thinking of something entirely different and slightly naughty. When they got to Jack, Baldwin released her arm and stood aside, like a father presenting a bride to the groom, and Jack, after a quick nod to Baldwin, took a step forward, put one hand on his rather expanded shirt-front, and gave Kitty a low, deep bow. She cocked her head, like a bird, and then responded with a long, deep curtsy, one of her ironic, Kittyesque curtsies which seemed to say, "This is a dumb thing to do, but while I'm doing it, I might as well go whole hog." Echoes of dancing school and Mr. Van Dam were almost palpable in the air, and people applauded once again.

Cooper noticed that, close up, Kitty didn't look quite so terrific. She was tan from Florida, and flushed from her snowy jaunt across half of New York state, but her arms were strikingly thin and there were darkish circles under her bright eyes. You probably couldn't tell she was sick, but you could see that she was now a fifty-year-old woman, with crow's feet, and a crepe neck, and widening hips, and blurry, dusty blond hair which spoke of too many trips to the beauty parlor. But she was still Kitty. No doubt about that.

The orchestra leader stood watchfully on the podium as the musicians adjusted the music on their stands. The television crews moved in for the kill. Kitty looked straight into one of the cameras and said, "Hey, we haven't had a chance to practice."

"I worked with the orchestra this afternoon," Jack said quietly, and to her.

"I did what I could in Florida," she said. "Some of it came back, some of it didn't."

"I worked out the basic moves," he said.

"Then lead on, MacDuff, and we'll hope for the best," said Kitty, and someone from the audience shouted "Yeah!" And there was another round of applause.

Everyone began moving off the floor, to settle at their tables or stand in groups along the side. The television people jockeyed their equipment into appropriate positions. The main entrance was now crowded with people from downstairs who had heard the cheering and applause and were pushing their way in to see what all the fuss was about. Cooper saw Saul and Judy Radner and the Downtown Rehabilitation Committee edge their way through the crowd. Waiters with trays and dishwashers with towels stood in the open kitchen door.

In this preparatory flurry, Kitty whispered to Cooper, "Get me a drink of water, my love, and I'm yours forever," and when he brought her one, he saw her take a quick pill before she handed back the cup. Then she and Jack moved to the center of the room and stood facing each other. The television people turned on their bright lights. "Doesn't anyone want to sing the 'Star Spangled Banner'?" said Kitty over her shoulder to no one in particular. Everyone laughed nervously. Then the conductor raised his baton, Kitty took a deep breath, Jack nodded at the orchestra, the conductor hit the downbeat, and they danced.

227

23

They danced. They made it. They got through the number, and they weren't bad. As Kitty had said, some of it came back and some of it didn't. Jack had none of his old jaunty confidence, but moved with the careful grace and containment of a heavier man. Kitty, who had always been so delectably late, was even later now, since she was tired, and half the time had no idea what she was doing. But she followed him. She put herself into his hands. It was a kind of gesture of faith on her part that she'd let him hold her, and catch her, and show her what to do next. And some of what they did was really quite astonishing, seeing as how they hadn't danced together in thirty years. The waltz section, for example, came back in all its glory and evoked a sudden volley of bravos from one side of the room. But in the Latin American interlude, they got hopelessly out of sync, and when they got to the tap-dancing part, they both looked downright silly. Still the orchestra stayed with them and helped them out, and when they went into their final cakewalk, and then their last dips and spins and twirls, they briefly were wonderful once again.

Cooper, who was watching with Liz and a group of the older people on one side of the room, was initially disappointed. But as the dance continued, he began to see what had made Jack and Kitty so compelling to him, what had kept them dancing in his memory all these many years. There they were, gliding over this resilient old floor in this refurbished old hotel in this gallant old town, as a grim winter storm raged outside: Jack serious, solemn, and intent; Kitty wry, ironic, and bemused. It was as if they knew, and were inviting everyone else to know, that all their dips and spins and breaks and turns were simply bright bubbles on a dark surface of sin, chaos, and death—and the best they could do, the best anyone could do, was to put a good face on things and dance. Cooper sensed this, and he thought Liz sensed it, and the people standing near him seemed to sense it too, and maybe that's why, when the dance was over, their particular group burst into such loud applause.

As for the rest of the audience—the young singles clustered together on the opposite side of the room, the waitresses by the door to the kitchen, various others—they responded adequately. Their applause was hardly deafening, but it was more than decent, more than polite. Even the people who were hanging out around the main door clapped, some of them, before they pushed their way out and back downstairs. Saul and Judy Radner came up to Cooper and shook his hand and said, "It was very good, Cooper. Excellent. Very impressive indeed," before they, too, rejoined the Winterfest.

There was a group of young people from boarding school who had rented evening clothes and come to the Snow Ball as a special favor to their parents. They now were loosening their ties and saying good-bye and figuring out where to go next.

"I don't think they were *that* great, Mummy," said Alice Anderson's daughter Jennifer, who was one of this gang.

"Well, then you simply can't appreciate good dancing," said Alice huffily, and walked away.

Jack and Kitty, of course, were delighted to have gotten through it. They were now surrounded by well-wishers who told them they were simply marvelous from beginning to end. You could tell they knew they weren't, but they appreciated being told they were. Both were perspiring and out of breath, and Kitty looked a little pale, so they were rushed to a table and given all sorts of things to drink. They sat there for a while, next to each other, talking to people who came and went, being hugged and kissed and patted on the back. They talked very little with each other. After about half an hour, Kitty whispered something to Baldwin Hall, who got up and said that Kitty had had a very long day and ought to go to bed.

Lucy Dunbar jumped to her feet and said her guest room was waiting and she'd drive them home immediately. Baldwin thanked her very much, but said he thought they'd check in right here at the hotel. It was easier, he said, and they had to be off early the next day.

So they said good-bye to everyone. Cooper and Lucy accompanied them to the top of the stairs, where Kitty turned and gave them both big hugs.

"So long, you two," she said. "It was fun."

Cooper held onto her hands. "You were great to come, Kitty. I mean it."

"I wanted to," Kitty said. "It kind of ties things up, after all."

But she said this a little distractedly because she had noticed Jack, who was now there too, looking at her in a strange, moony way. "Oh, yeah," she said. "And you."

"You were wonderful, Kitty," he said in a thick voice.

"Well we tried, anyway, didn't we?" said Kitty, smiling, and she held out her hand. They shook hands and that was that.

The Snow Ball began to break up soon after. Jack did his duty dances with Liz and with Lucy, and then established himself around the bar. The saxophone player from the orchestra joined him after the musicians folded their tents.

"You go on without me," he said to Cooper, who was getting tired. "I'll get home somehow."

"I'll get him home," said the saxophone player.

So Cooper thanked him profusely, and told him to call tomorrow whenever he felt like it and they'd "do something." The maids and sweepers were already beginning to clean up, so Cooper, who still felt somewhat like a host, thanked them too, and then left with Liz.

Downstairs, Winterfest was still going strong. A rock band was blasting away at one end of the lobby, and a lot of young people—including the preppy contingent from up above—were bouncing around to the beat. Near the stairs, Cooper and Liz had to weave their way through a noisy crowd of people who were pushing and shoving in front of a booth which served fast Chinese food.

A heavyset man shouted at Cooper. "Hey, you! Hey, you in the monkey suit! What's going on upstairs?"

"Oh, just a party," Cooper said. "It's over now."

A young punk, of indiscriminate color and accent, called over, "I was up there. Nothing but some fat guy pushing an old broad around the room."

"You have no idea what you're talking about," said Cooper, and he and Liz moved on through the crowd.

Outside, the storm had stopped. The air was crisp and clear. Above the new Marine Midland Building, there were even a few stars. The snow crunched under their feet as they made their way single file, Liz first, through the winding paths to their car. They could see their breaths.

They were almost to the parking lot when Cooper felt a hand slam down on his shoulder from behind. He wheeled around and there was the young hood he had just spoken to indoors.

"Hey, man," said the hood. "What you say to me in there?"

"I said you didn't know what you were talking about," said Cooper.

"That's what I thought you said." The punk gave him a shove in the chest.

Cooper almost lost his balance in the narrow path. "Now wait a minute . . . "

But the punk shoved him again, and as Cooper tripped and sat down in a snowbank, he saw Liz trudging on into the parking lot, unaware of what was happening behind her.

Now the punk was standing over him. "Still think I don't know nothing, man?"

Cooper struggled to his feet, feeling almost ludicrous as he tried to get some purchase in the snow. There was nothing to do but fight. He swung at the guy, missed completely, and then reeled back as he felt a fist land on the side of his face. He threw himself forward, and now they were both falling and rolling in the deep snow beside the path, grunting, swearing, punching whenever they could. Cooper had the weight and protection of his heavy overcoat, but the punk was quick, wiry, and obviously at home in a fight.

Even as they struggled, Cooper was taken back to almost forty years ago, to one of those fights he used to have in the men's cloakroom before dancing school, around on the floor before Mr. Van Dam came in and broke it up.

Then suddenly they were both covered, buried, drowned as great heaps of snow kept landing on their faces, and they had to separate and struggle to the surface and brush the snow from their faces in order to breathe.

Cooper sat up and saw Liz standing over them with a snow shovel, ready to toss another load on them both. She was intervening once again.

"Go home," she said to the punk. "Go away. Go somewhere, or I'll have you arrested under Title Five."

"He insulted me," said the punk, wiping his eyes. Cooper saw that he was just a kid, about the age of his older son.

"Just go," said Liz, brandishing the shovel. So the kid struggled to his feet and went.

"What's Title Five?" asked Cooper as she helped him up.

"I have no idea," said Liz, brushing him off.

She guided him over the last piles of snow into the parking lot and leaned the shovel neatly against the door of the empty attendant's shack where she had found it. Then she helped him into the car and brushed the snow off the front and back windshields so she could see to drive him home. The city looked lovely in the snow, even to Cooper, even then: fresh, new, and clean.

In the bathroom mirror, after his hot shower, Cooper could see that he wasn't terribly hurt. He'd probably have a shiner tomorrow, and a swollen cheek, but that was about it. Liz brought him up some herb tea, and as they sat on the bed, he said he had some things he wanted to talk to her about, things that had happened over the past year.

Liz said she'd had enough of the past for one day, frankly, and she was dog tired. If he'd just concentrate on finishing that tea, and maybe take an aspirin to calm down, they could turn out the light and get some sleep.

24

The next day, Cooper hung around the house, licking his wounds so to speak, and waiting for a call from Jack. One of his sons was still home and wanted to know what had happened to his face.

"I slipped and fell on the ice," Cooper said.

"That's a lie," said Liz. "Your father got into a fight defending the Snow Ball." And she told the whole story as sympathetically as she could. Cooper's son was very impressed with Cooper, and Cooper was very impressed with Liz.

Later, about noon, he telephoned Jack's mother, who said that Jack had stopped by for his bags earlier that morning.

"He was out all night," said Jack's mother. "Staying with friends."

Lucy called a little later to say that Kitty and Baldwin had checked out of the George Washington very early too.

"I thought I might be able to drive Jack to the airport," she said, "but I couldn't locate him, either."

"Everybody knew when to leave, all right," said Cooper. "I suppose that's a good thing."

"I couldn't agree more," said Lucy, and that's pretty much all she said before they hung up.

The following Monday evening, on the six o'clock news, one of the television stations apparently devoted several minutes to "Friday night's festivities downtown."

Cooper didn't see it because he was playing squash with Saul Radner, nor did Liz, who was driving home from work, nor did Lucy, who was at her desk trying to compose a letter to Cooper, saying that she sensed their relationship was cooling rapidly, and maybe it was just as well. But those who happened to turn it on told Cooper that the broadcast devoted much too much time to the hullabaloo downstairs, and very little to Jack and Kitty. They did have one shot of them, dancing blurrily in the distance, but they were so far away it was hard to tell much of anything.

The Indianapolis station did nothing at all about it, according to Carol Graham who lived there and who watched the television like a hawk. There was one picture in the paper of Jack arriving at the airport—"Lieutenant Governor seeks roots in Buffalo"—but that was about it. Carol did write that there were rumors his marriage was in trouble, and later on in the year, it was published in the Buffalo *News* that Jack's wife had sued for divorce on the grounds of "basic incompatibility."

Jack's family difficulties cost him the nomination for the governorship in March. Some people argued that he still could have won it if he had campaigned harder, but apparently the steam had gone out of him in the new year. *The New York Times* reported that he made a fine, stalwart speech of withdrawal, gazing directly into the television cameras and beaming winningly as his rival came forward to shake his hand. He left Indianapolis when the new administration came in, and a few years later somebody heard he was running a chain of liquor stores in Phoenix, Arizona, and supposedly was doing quite well.

Kitty had died by then. Baldwin Hall called Cooper from Ocean Reef in June and told him the sad news. She'd had a tough time, but was a good sport all the way, and according to Baldwin, held on long after the doctors thought she would go. Good old Kitty, late at the last. Cooper couldn't help but imagine her curtsying ironically in front of the Grim Reaper and saying, "Eeek. Help. Here I am. What am I supposed to do now?"

There was talk of having a memorial service for her in Buffalo—in the ballroom of the George Washington, at the Saturn Club, *somewhere*—but no one took the reins and pretty soon it was too late. Baldwin brought her ashes back in the middle of the summer, and Cooper got Paul Lovewell from Trinity Church to say a few words before she was buried in her family plot out at Forest Lawn.

Cooper and Liz continued to argue about almost everything except their children. Once again they began to form a solid wall as they tried to nudge their brood into getting married and settling down and producing some *grandchildren*, for God's sake, before it was too late. Lucy Dunbar started taking courses out at the university and fell in love with an Iranian dissident, ten years younger than she was.

They subsequently moved to Minneapolis, where apparently she's having a perfectly wonderful time.

No one ever again tried to revive the Snow Ball. It was over, done with, kaput, though it was still talked about on occasion. As time went on, it became quite the thing to say you had been there, at the last one, when Jack Daley had danced with Kitty Price for the last time. "Oh, they were good, they were great, they were wonderful," people began to say as they looked back, even those younger people who had drifted so dissappointedly downstairs. Cooper Jones said so too. All right, maybe it was just a fat guy pushing an old broad around the room, but Cooper also remembered, swirling about them, dipping and turning, a stalwart young man and a classy young woman, he wonderfully deliberate, she deliciously late, Jack and Kitty, dancing together on into the night.